BEYOND

THE

LIGHT BARRIER

The Autobiography

of Elizabeth Klarer

The romantic story of the encounter
between a South African woman and
a man from Meton, a planet in
Proxima Centauri

BEY●ND
THE
LIGHT BARRIER

*The Autobiography
of Elizabeth Klarer*

Light Technology Publishing
Flagstaff, Arizona

ISBN-10: 1-891824-77-5
ISBN-13: 978-1-891824-77-7

Light Technology Publishing, LLC
Phone: 800-450-0985
Fax: 928-714-1132
PO Box 3540
Flagstaff, AZ 86003
www.lighttechnology.com

DEDICATION

To the memory of my sister, May Flower, who struggled for existence in a hostile world, and dedicated with love to Akon, who made it possible for this book to be written.

ACKNOWLEDGMENTS

During the past twenty-one years I have had the assistance of many hundreds of South Africans, foreign citizens and officials to whom I would like to express my gratitude.

My deepest appreciation and gratitude to Mr. Hollidge and Mr. Tucker of Mathison & Hollidge, whose wonderful and unforgettable kindness, generosity, interest and care in my welfare have given me the time and strength to create this beautiful book. I also wish to thank and express my deep appreciation to Karl and Anny Veit, who gave their selfless cooperation in the publication of this book, and for the inestimable value of Manfred Landeck's translation—he was tuned to my frequency.

I wish to express my deep appreciation to the late Air Chief Marshal Lord Dowding. I also express appreciation to Dr. Meiring Naude (Scientific Adviser to the Prime Minister), Professor Tusinius, Professor Wilson (International Liaison Lawyer and Jurisconsultant to the British Institute), the South African Air Force, South African Security Police, Major and Mrs. Jock Flower and Major Aubrey Fielding (British Intelligence MI-10) for their valued encouragement and help.

A special tribute is due to SABC, SABC-TV and the South African press. I wish to thank all the broadcasters and members of the press who have supported me and given publicity to this book, among many of them: Mrs. Joy Anderson, Mrs. Doreen Levin, Chris Vermaak, Richard Gibbs, Jan deWaal, Hilary Prendini, Petra Pieterse, Colonel

Stephen Grenfell of the BBC, the Argus Group of newspapers, the Citizen and Fair Lady Magazines, Hoofstad, Dagbreek and many other news media.

Finally, I want to express my love and gratitude to my daughter, Dr. Marilyn Phillips; my son, David Klarer; my sister, Mrs. Barbara McKenzie; my dearest friend, Mrs. Neslie Schmutz; and Mrs. Stephanie Mellis, who understood and supported my aspirations. I also want to thank our very dear Gus, Mrs. Augusta Sell, for giving me her thoughtful care, and to Geoff and Lynette Wilson for giving me such a lovely home to live in.

TABLE OF CONTENTS

TIME ON THE COSMIC LEVEL...xi
FOREWORD: A SYMBOL OF MAN REACHING FOR THE MOON xiii

CHAPTER 1: A STRANGER IN OUR SKIES.. 1
CHAPTER 2: LINK WITH MEN OF OTHER WORLDS 13
CHAPTER 3: THE SECRETS OF LIGHT..21
CHAPTER 4: AN ESCAPE ROUTE TO THE STARS................................41
CHAPTER 5: THE HEIGHTS OF CATHKIN 69
CHAPTER 6: BEYOND THE TIME BARRIER: TO ALPHA CENTAURI 115
CHAPTER 7: THE NATURE OF THE UNIVERSE.................................159

EPILOGUE: THE ALPHA AND OMEGA OF ALL THINGS.............................179

BOOK MARKET 189

TIME ON THE COSMIC LEVEL

T his book is about time on the cosmic level, with new data not yet
registered on scientific instruments. The reader needs to follow
the cosmic layout of my writing very closely to understand the vast
implications involved. Otherwise, the cosmic scale of this book will be lost
and misunderstood by many whose intelligence cannot be expanded in this
epoch of time to a conscious awareness of our cosmic connections.

—Elizabeth Klarer
A.T.C.L.
Dipl.Met., Cambridge

The most beautiful and most profound emotion we can experience is the sensation of the mystical. It is the sower of all true science. He to whom this emotion is a stranger, who can no longer wonder and stand rapt in awe, is as good as dead. To know that what is impenetrable to us really exists, manifesting itself as the highest wisdom and the most radiant beauty which our dull primitive can comprehend only in their primitive forms—this knowledge, this feeling is at the center of true religiousness.

—Albert Einstein

Ikhanya elikhanya emnyameni.
(A light that enlightened the darkness.)

—Zulu praise

A SYMBOL OF MAN REACHING
FOR THE MOON

" . . . and he was also a symbol . . . a symbol of man reaching for the moon
and the stars, of man flashing into space in an endless adventure . . . "

For as long as man has lived in this world, from the days when he
lived in a cave, he has searched for knowledge. He has reached
the heights of Everest, the depths of the sea. His aircraft in thousands span the globe and gradually encircle this Earth at greater heights
and greater speeds, making of what was a vast circumference something
that is so puny that it is not surprising that he is reaching out into the vast,
limitless, uncharted fields of space.

He has reached the moon, the first stage of his journey to other civilizations on other worlds—for make no mistake, we are not alone. This is now
proven by archaeologists, scientists and astronomers. The pace of discovery
is heightening now that the clues have been established. Almost every day
brings amazing and exciting discoveries. Other civilizations from whence
we came are out there, and it is there that man's future must lie.

Some years ago, when in British Intelligence in Malaya—fighting
the communist bandits hidden in the vast jungles—one felt a sense of
awful frustration. Nowhere in the world was there peace. The whole
Earth was torn by strife, Cold War and hot war. Thousands of people
said, "Man is making such a mess of life; there is such turmoil. Is it really
worth living?"

At the time, an Oxford professor came out and lectured to us. He said: "There are masses of Mother Grundies saying, 'What a dreadful age in which to live!' Do these people realize what a wonderful age it is? We are on the very threshold of leaving this planet and traveling and exploring the vast universe. . . . This is the beginning."

He went on to describe the ramjet, or flying stovepipe, as he described it—just a heated stovepipe that would soon project men through space at ever-increasing speeds. A dreadful age indeed! How fortunate we are to be alive, and what wonderful, enthralling achievements we may see in our lifetimes.

These pages tell, through personal experience, of an advanced civilization in outer space, a civilization that has already found the secrets of space propulsion. One is enthralled at the beauty and wonder of their silent electrical ships that hover over and have landed on this Earth.

Purely imaginary, one might say, until one reads the immense amount of scientific and technical explanation given by the author. The defeat of so-called gravity has long been a dream, with weightlessness being the answer. This, it seems, can only be achieved in the electrical field, and here it is described in absorbing detail for the scientist or the man in the street to perceive. It is indeed true to say that he who first achieves the answers will be complete master of this Earth.

But these people from space are not only advanced in the scientific field; they are physically, mentally and spiritually evolved and wish to bring nothing but good to this planet. Let us hope that before man is given the secret, he too will want to take with him peace and goodwill and not the present strife and evils of this Earth. Why, whenever there is a reported landing, must people rush for firearms in a panic and start blazing away? Because it is man's instinct of self-preservation and destruction.

May we fly peacefully into the unknown one day. May the space people come to us and show us a better way of life before we destroy ourselves and the world. Not only is there technical detail in all fields in this book, but the beauty of universal love as described by the author—who is certainly no ordinary person herself—will never be forgotten.

Anthony Fielding, Major
British Intelligence Corps (retired)

CHAPTER 1

A STRANGER IN OUR SKIES

We were feeding our Sealyham puppies in the stableyard when we saw it. The Sun had just gone down behind the Drakensberg and the early summer sky of the Natal midlands was clear and rain-washed after the storm had passed. The guinea fowl were calling to each other as they prepared to roost in the wattle tree that grew near the house. Suddenly, they stopped calling—and my sister and I both saw it at the same time.

An enormous silvery disk swooped down toward us, moving with a changing brightness out of the clear expanse of sky—a globe of light as clear as a pearl. Fascinated, we watched it maneuver over us, while the puppies left their food and ran yelping into the kennel.

Then suddenly another huge sphere fell out of the sky, rolling down toward us, glowing orange-red and rotating slowly as it came, pockmarked with craters like the Moon. A fiery and terrifying planetoid was silently and gracefully sweeping through the upper reaches of Earth's atmosphere, and as it slowly rotated, suspended on its course toward us, the silvery disk moved with a flash of light and paced beside it in a slow passage across the sky until the planetoid moved out of the Sun's rays to the north, leaving a long, thick trail like smoke across the heavens.

We both ran for the house, my heart thumping so loudly against my ribs that I was quite breathless when we reached the wide verandah where our parents were sitting, enjoying the evening tranquillity. My sister told them what we had seen in breathless snatches of excitement—two small children with white, excited faces trying to tell of something fantastic in the sky. My father got up and walked to the edge of the long verandah and looked up into the sky.

"Perhaps it was a meteor," he said.

The wide stoep, peculiar to South African farmhouses, hid the sky with its sloping roof, and the view was across a beautiful expanse of lawns with great oaks and pine trees; the home park with brilliant flowers in long beds, azaleas and rhododendrons massed among the trees; and beyond, to the hills and the mountains of the Dragon.

"No, no," I insisted when I got my breath again. "Something out there saved Earth, our beautiful planet, from a ravening, desolate asteroid intent on a collision course and destruction."

I paused, and then said, "And—something out there, a beautiful spaceship from elsewhere—came in time to see our plight."

"In time?" my father gently queried. "How do you know?"

"Yes . . . I know . . ." And putting my hand in my mother's, I went indoors with her to have supper. My mother's great gift of understanding was an everlasting joy to me, as in that moment the vibrations of time drew aside the nebulous mists of eternity and the womb of the future revealed itself to my questing soul.

The grown-ups' dinner was much later, and when my mother came to kiss us good night, she had changed into a flowing gown of shimmering gold. Maintaining the civilized standards of her aristocratic English background even in the distances of the African veld, she brought the gracious way of life inherited from her noble family.

Too excited to sleep, I lay awake listening to the heavenly music of Mozart as my mother played the Bechstein boudoir grand in the distant drawing room. Her magic touch on the keyboard liberated my soul to the heights of heaven as I relaxed and looked up through the wide-open window into the starry sky and wondered if we would see the beautiful spaceship again.

THE YEAR OF HALLEY'S COMET

I was born in the year of Halley's Comet, at the other farm set in the rolling thorn country overlooking the vast distances of the lowveld, where the Mooi River meets the mighty Tugela in surroundings of startling beauty.

The still nights of the full moon were filled with the rhythmic stamping and chanting of the Zulu, and the rhythm of the drums, rising and fading in volume, beat like a heart through the moonlit distances of the thornveld.

When we moved to the new farm in the foothills of the Drakensberg, Ladam, the *induna¹*, came with us. He refused to stay behind in the thornveld where it was much warmer. He was an *ikhelha²* and all would listen to his advice and words of wisdom, and he would not allow us to go elsewhere without him to take care of us. He rode the many kilometers on the gray mare my father had given him and appeared like a wraith in the stableyard as a howling blizzard swept down from the mountains of the Dragon.

In the beautiful rolling grass country of the Drakensberg foothills, I was allowed more freedom, and after lessons I would catch my pony and canter away to the solitude of the hills, often going to my favorite hilltop overlooking the farmstead in the valley. The pony would roll and then enjoy the evergreen grass within the bowl or dip at the top of the hill, browsing to her heart's content, while I would lie in the thick grass, watching the sky in the hope of seeing the never-to-be-forgotten spaceship my sister and I had seen from the stableyard in the valley below. Little did I realize what this hilltop would mean to me in years to come.

WHERE THE SKY JOINS THE EARTH AT THE HORIZON

Ladam would watch me go with the knowledge of centuries in his wise old eyes and send an *umfana³* to watch and see that no danger befell me. There were always eyes, though—herdboys and *abafana⁴* lying in the long grass as still as mice or swaying in the branches of a tree or squatting in an outcrop of rocks. Nothing ever goes unseen. All is known. This faculty, which is born and bred in the African veld, spreads its influence to the white children conceived within its embrace.

Ladam always called me by my Zulu name.

"*Hlangabeza⁵, Inkosazana⁶*," raising his hand in salute, and my mother looked at me with wondering eyes.

1. *headman*
2. *man in late middle age*
3. *boy*
4. *small boys*
5. *to meet*
6. *little chieftainess*

"To meet—one who brings together," he explained to my mother.

"The golden hair of her head will bring the *Abelungu*[1] from the sky, and there will be a meeting together," Ladam said. "They are the sky gods who once lived on this world, but afterward ascended to the sky over our heads by means of the spider's thread in clouds of lightning and thunder."

Then he would tell me in the expressive language of the Zulu about the folklore of his people while I sat on the garden wall. I could understand the Zulu tongue, and I listened while he unfolded the folklore of his tribe, which was more enthralling and fascinating than any tale from elsewhere. I sensed his sincere belief and the ring of truth in his narrative, and I would glance up into the depths of the blue sky with wondering eyes as he told of many strange and mysterious things.

"Once upon a time, a man and a woman came down from the sky on a cloud and alighted upon a hilltop. They were white and shining, with hair of gold. Their village is said to be lighted by a mightier light than any on this world. The people wear shining clothes and the huts are thatched with shining grass. They were caught up to heaven again by a flash of lightning.

They are goodly to look on, beautiful and radiant—their clans are taller and lighter-complexioned and markedly different in feature. These heaven dwellers will return with the lightning bird whose scales glitter in many colors. It is blue or gold, or it is red or green like a metallic iridescence. And when you are a grown woman, you will go to the mountaintop and there you will wait for the heaven dwellers and there will be a meeting together, a mating. You belong to the heaven dwellers. We know this. The *mfiti*[2] has told us.

"There," he said with a long, drawn-out breath and pointed a gnarled finger. "There, on the mountaintop, the lightning bird whose blue and gold scales glitter in many colors like the rainbow will come for you, *Inkosazana*. The heaven dwellers used to live here in a big land far to the south, but afterward ascended to the sky by means of the spider's thread from the lightning bird. Some of our people have gotten into the heaven country by climbing a mountain or a tree, ascending by means of a rope uncoiling from a cloud, or by the thread the spider obligingly spins for

1. *white people*
2. *witch*

them. The Zulu say, 'Who can plait a rope for ascending, that he may go to heaven.' Into the sky for Zulu means 'the sky,' and we Zulu have long had a high opinion of ourselves to be tall like the sky and not mingle with the lesser tribes of black peoples. Our destiny lies in the proud aggression of our *Izimpi*[1], who await the return of our sky gods.

"Cattle and horses were sent down from the heaven country for the sustenance of the Zulu. Only white cattle and white horses were sent, but the horses died of a fever in our country, and the few that were left raced away one day before the great wind of a storm, while the cattle flourished and became as numerous as *Inyonikai pumuli*[2]. And when the big drought came, we turned to eating the flesh of the white cattle for sustenance, and by so doing became a warlike people.

"The spirits of our ancestors remain in a village in the center of the world, and clumps of tall trees beside mountain tarns show the way to the underworld. These trees are cared for and venerated. The ghost country can only be reached through caves or holes in the ground, and it is not usual for the heaven dwellers to be found in the company of the underground dwellers by the slope where the sky joins the earth at the horizon.

"There is also the *Tokoloshe*[3] who comes out of the ground to make unlawful love to women. He can live in the water, and it is said that this being has been seen on the banks of the Umzinduzi River near Umkambati, beyond Pietermaritzburg."

THERE WAS NO SOUND, ONLY COMPLETE SILENCE.

As Ladam told me of these things, the Sun dimmed as sudden, scudding clouds swept across its disk. A black cloud gathered to the east with sudden jagged flashes of forked lightning playing about its flat base. As the menacing cloud moved closer, I cried out with delight as we both saw the great silvery spaceship glowing with a white radiance against the awesome cumulonimbus. The terrible, broad funnel of a tornado began to form from the base of the cloud, swaying and twisting as it reached downward toward the ground, moving swiftly and haphazardly along its destructive path and heading up the valley toward the homestead.

---

1. *Zulu army*
2. *The white birds that have no rest.*
3. *A being with a short, hairy body.*

Attracted by the deafening roar of the mature tornado, my mother's anxious face appeared at the drawing room windows. I saw the sudden wonder in her eyes as she caught a glimpse of the spaceship moving across the terrifying tornado, and the broad funnel swayed as it lifted over us. Looking up, my awestruck eyes beheld the interior of the great funnel.

Swaying gently and bending slowly toward the east, filled with the pale blue light of electricity, it stood motionless over us save for a slow up-and-down pulsation. Higher up, the funnel was partly filled with a bright cloud that shimmered like a fluorescent light. This brilliant cloud was in the middle, not touching the smooth, rotating walls, which looked as if it were composed of rings moving one behind the other, rippling down toward the rim in a wave motion. It pulsed like a live thing, and as the higher ring moved onward, the ring immediately below slipped over to get back under it.

I found myself involuntarily responding to the rhythm of the great rings as the pulsebeats in my head kept time with their wave motion. Yet there was no sound, only complete silence, and as the wave motion reached the bottom of the circle, the far rim of the funnel jerked downward and long, vaporous, pale blue streamers extended out and upward from the roof of the house. And then the thick opaque rim passed over without touching the house or the surrounding trees.

A few feet further on, the rippling motion within the funnel jerked downward and flicked a tall pine tree away like a flash of light! When the funnel touched it, the tree dissolved, the parts shooting off to the right like sparks. Again the funnel touched down, demolishing an empty shed, and with a frightening roar, spent its fury in the hills beyond.

Ladam's face had aged in those few moments of sudden danger. Shaking his head with awe, he explained that the heaven dwellers and their lightning bird with glittering silver scales had come to save us again as they had done that evening many months back. Therefore, the *mfiti* was telling the truth.

HUMANKIND IS NOT UNIQUE

The angry cloud had not finished with us. As I ran into the house, a ball of lightning surrounded by a glowing blue haze moved along the telephone wires into the house. It squeezed past me through the doorway and out into the garden as if it had a mind of its own. The fiery sphere swiftly moved along the ground like a creeping corona discharge in the electric field and then shot up the bole of an oak tree, returning to the serrated cloud base above in a flash of lightning. Bits of bark scattered through the open doorway, and the whiplash crack of the lightning channel's explosive shock waves knocked me sprawling on the polished floor.

My Siamese cat sprang to my aid, spitting defiance at the elements beyond the door, her feline sensitivity outraged by the sudden proximity of magnetic lines of force. Emotionally disturbed, she padded about the hall and refused to be comforted until I gathered her up in my arms and ran through the house to a more neutral spot.

Ladam called the beautiful grass-covered uplands where our homestead nestled *Mpofana*, a musical name well suited to the rolling hills where the long grass sings in the south wind. "Good horse country," my father said, where he could breed the white horses so dear to his heart. I would watch them gallop with the wind that blows down ahead of an approaching storm, drinking the wind like Mohammed's sacred white mare, or like Pegasus, whose real home is in the upper sky, where one must go upon wings to see it.

It was here that Selene was born and given to me, a true daughter of the wind. Tossing her delicate head and turning to me with gentle affection, nudging her soft muzzle into my back, she would stand in the open doorway of her loose box, the classic curve of her head outlined against the darkness within like snow upon the blue molecules of the sky.

Her ancient lineage is lost in the mists of time—there is no trace in the history of the past to indicate the origin of her white ancestors. Could it be the stony uplands of an arid land where first they set hoof on earth to gladden the hearts of men? Or perhaps from the empty coolness of a cloud drawing the golden chariot of Helios, as the white horses pranced across the aura of the Sun coming to Earth as a culmination of the Sun's rays, where white is the great principle of light from the farthest spiral galaxy to the minutest micro-atoms within the atoms?

Bred in the cradle wind of heaven, the snowy-white horses brought to Earth the graceful rhythm of dancing snowflakes. They moved with the vibrations of time in perfection of composition as only the soaring imagination of Mozart could conjure. Mozart, who brought the majesty and peace of heaven to Earth in a life of sublime creation, whose life was cut short, destroyed by an envier whose dark and sinister intent is inherent in mortal man. What legacy of immortal music could there have been for humankind had he been allowed to live, had he not been poisoned by the black alchemy of the age?

The unearthly white horses are a legacy for humankind. In this age of mechanization and frightening technology, people of Earth are merely human beings while each horse is unique—a genius of its species, an elemental force, like a dream in the drab emptiness of our time. As they tread the soil of Earth in the rolling high grass country of Mpofana, perhaps there is a similarity to the heady atmosphere of the stony uplands of yore, when Earth was younger and closer to her star and the planet of their origin. Ladam had said the white horses came from the heaven country, and these are their descendants.

I looked into the mysterious sky, remote and never still, and wondered about Nature's plan for men of Earth. Will they ever grasp and understand her plan of evolution set for them? Will they realize one day that the whole universe in which they have their being is life, composed of energy and matter, and that they are merely a part of its condensed energy? Humankind is not unique. He is merely a creature of the cosmos who is still too immature to comprehend the profound truth of his origin—his galactic origin. Perhaps a race memory, nourished and retained within his subconscious through centuries of Earth time, may burst forth in the splendor of truth when he treads the road to the stars and returns into the fold of the universe in which he has his being.

THE MAGIC OF THE LODESTONE IS THE BASIS OF ALL LIFE.

Growing up and going to live overseas to further my studies could not dim the memory of the great silver spaceship hovering in the mysterious sky. Unconsciously I would look up into the depths of blue, hoping, hoping, my eyes clouding with tears I could not restrain, as a snatch of music or a sunset in the sky would cause me suddenly to catch my breath in memory.

Even marriage and the birth of my first child could not ease my longing. My husband chided me on being so restless and flew me into the sky in a Tiger Moth biplane, teaching me how to fly. Encouraged by his understanding, I would fly off into the depths of blue, seeking the ship of space in her own environment.

The hazards in the sky were few and the lovely days clear with endless vision. I headed toward the Drakensberg with the rolling green hills spread out beneath. Only an isolated thundercloud prowled to the west. Suddenly, I was struck by a volley of hailstones out of the sunlit sky. The beautiful white anvil cloud that was soaring innocently in the sky spewed a barrage of ice across the blue from its scarflike fringe.

I instantly banked away to escape, but the angry cloud had not finished with me. It released a bolt from the blue. Lightning rapped the top of my head and ran through my hands into the control column. Pale green sparks jumped in front of my eyes and soft bluish tongues of light played about the wingtips and propeller, forming an eerie corona about the little craft diving through the air while the muttering thundercloud prowled on, looking for something new on which to vent its spleen.

Lightning is only dangerous when one is in contact with Earth, and if one depends on thunderstorm manners and behavior in the great presence, there is no need to be afraid at all. I soon learned to love and become one with the whirling thunderheads, though I always kept my distance. Great swirling clouds—their cells growing, fusing and multiplying in a chain reaction of exploding cumulus—would spring up like amoebas, generation by generation, moving across the face of Earth. I, with my tiny plane, would find a safe cloud canyon through which to fly, or I would pass to the left to avoid headwinds while the thunderhead boiled upward until the frigid heights flattened its top and the wind tapered it to a leeward point.

I found happiness in the sky. I loved to feel the wind high in the sky as the plane soared through the ocean of air to sense the rhythm of the wind as the airy depths became a fluid mass that I could see, understand and trust—to go with the wind or against it, and to know which is the lee side of a range or hill, for there is danger on the lee side when flying with the wind.

For us who see from the distances in the sky with the clean fresh wind blowing in our faces, truth is the messenger of joy, an understanding of the soul toward the firmament beyond. To tune into the vibrations and waves on certain combinations of harmonics, to listen for the cosmic celesta, is to release the elusive magic of truth.

It was glorious to move through the uncharted sky, threading a way through the depths of air, the substance of which the sky is made, where the clouds float in all their glory and the wind is the spirit of the sky's third dimension. There, the forces of magnetism permeate all matter and all life and the connection between magnetism and the mind is a reality, while in the geomagnetic field there is an affinity with the universe, which is the source of all telepathic thought.

The magic of the lodestone is the basis of all life. It holds the stars and planets in place and is responsible for their birth and evolution, pervading our entire world in an affinity with the galaxy.

I Could Sense an Affinity beyond Normal Human Conception.

High in the sky, one can see the whole—the mountains and the sea beyond with the faint envelope of air that wraps the Earth. At sunset, the Earth's shadow rises in the east, steadily mounting the sky as a blue darkness, a prelude to the many-hued stars of the cosmic spectrum. High in the sky I sensed the nearness of something alien. I responded to a telepathic power beyond the mysterious sky. As I droned homeward through the flute note of the wind, my thoughts became a conviction and my mind responded to this mysterious power like a barometer.

Then one evening the mysterious stranger in our sky returned, and I knew my mind was being influenced as we flew over the Drakensberg. I was flying with my husband in a DH Leopard Moth from Durban to Baragwanath. The weather was clear and the Drakensberg lay ahead, stretching across the skyline, a rugged wall of darkness against the golden yellow of the sun's longer wavelengths. We were soon over the escarpment, our engine roaring in the strain of sudden turbulence. Above us, the southern skies had lost the pink counterglow that heralded the dark azure blue of Earth's shadow in the east. It rose as a huge arch to fill the whole sky with the fathomless velvet of darkest space, studded with stars and planets blazing out as beacons to their own part of creation.

Looking toward the east for Spica, which was rising over the horizon in virginal splendor, I was spellbound by another sphere flashing out of the dark azure of Earth's shadow. It was blue-white and pulsating, and it moved with incredible velocity straight for our tiny, helpless plane.

I tapped my husband on the back of his neck. He looked around and saw the enormous craft slow its speed, changing color to a brassy yellow as it leveled out and paced our plane. Fascinated, I observed every detail as I pressed my nose against the starboard window, seeing the bright hazy outline of the great circular ship as it paced alongside. Three portholes, shedding a softer glow, looked out from the side of a dome that sloped up from a vast hull. Beneath the hull, an intense blue-white light alternated with deepest violet, and no sound reached my ears above the frightened roar of the DH Moth.

Suddenly the great ship flipped onto its side, rolling along like a vast wheel, and then, with a brilliance of intensified light emanation, it disappeared—vanished!

"How wonderful!" I exclaimed into the headset.

"It was uncanny," my husband said. "As I banked away from the craft, it still maintained the same distance."

I was not afraid, though I felt as if a magnetic force was influencing my mind. I was sure that we had been thoroughly examined. The craft was the same type of spaceship I had seen as a child, and again, something known flashed into my mind. I found myself longing for its return, and a deep sense of loneliness mysteriously flooded my soul when the great ship vanished into the velvet darkness of the sky.

Looking down, I could just discern the vast contours of the Drakensberg. *Quathlamba* is the Zulu name for this beautiful mountain range lying like a sleeping giant so close to the sea—rugged and mysterious, still hiding the secrets of the universe. Precipitous cliffs, knife-edged against the glow in the west, merged into soft and steep slopes mantled in long green grass, sweeping on as rolling hills to the sea, the mountain peaks guarding the lush softness of a shadowed land—the rolling grass country of Mpofana where I was born.

Dangerous crosswinds threw our light plane about, and I thought that Saint Christopher must have pulled strings for us so that we did not end up in a spin over the mountains when my husband had banked and dived to avoid the spaceship. Spica winked at me out of the eastern sky, her lucid glory undimmed, pulsing, flashing blue-white and green, warning of a change in the weather and beckoning us to our rightful course. My mind was far away and filled with a great wonder. Again, the fantastic spaceship had appeared over the same area and I could sense an affinity beyond normal human conception.

With our flight plan completed at Baragwanath, we landed in the teeth of a southeast gale. Visibility was nil as mine dust blew from the dumps.

"Spica warned me," I said. "We were extremely lucky to land in one piece."

But all my husband could think about was that thing in the sky. He immediately made a detailed report to Air Force Headquarters in Pretoria.

What Do the Experts Know about the Sky?

I remained silent during the interrogation, because I knew they would not understand my feelings in the matter. Military men were unable to cope with such thoughts as mine, but I knew without any shadow of doubt that here was something new, something to break all the rules, something outside the realm of ordinary Earth people—a spaceship of revolutionary design, with an advanced method of propulsion. Had I not seen this same spaceship swoop down over my sister and me years before—and again, moving against that ominous tornado cloud—long before any nation on Earth could perfect such a craft?

What do the experts know about the sky? The secret heights still elude humanity's questing mind. My woman's intuition told me this was an alien ship from the far reaches of outer space. After that, my days of freedom were limited, as my husband packed us away in a ship for England. There, we became a part of the de Havilland Experimental Flight Center.

CHAPTER 2

LINK WITH MEN OF OTHER WORLDS

T he plane came in low, streaking across the landing field like a
bat out of hell. Shivering, I tried to turn away, but the icy wind
pinned me to the verge of the misty field. The long grass, sodden
with moisture, penetrated my gillie shoes with every step.

"How can he land at such speed? He could crash," I said to the wind
as the tiny craft disappeared into the murk of the English day.

The north wind cut through me, and the blue clouds tossed their dark
skirts across the sky, full of the whisperings of snow as the fat yellow clouds
banked to the east. Reading the writing in the sky, I watched with relief as
the shadowy form of the aircraft emerged far out on the field. She taxied
toward the haven of the hangar, her engine pulsating with rhythmic wholeness in the lull of the wind. Flurries of snow swept past as the pilot turned
her nose into the hangar entrance and the ground crew surrounded her. The
full-throated, whining roar of her engine died to silence as the pilot, ham-
pered by cumbersome fur-lined boots and a sheepskin jacket, slowly climbed
out of the cockpit. He stood wearily beside the aircraft for a moment, then
yielded to the backroom boffins. Their excitement was electric, but he shook
them off like an impatient bear and strode toward me, taking my arm in a
vice-like grip and pulling me along with the momentum of his stride.

"It's a miracle," he muttered. "She handled like a bird up there above
the clouds, and her landing speed is higher than anything tested before.
Thank God I did the flight plan myself! She is a wonder plane."

The pilot's enthusiasm for the aircraft entrusted to his skill overcame his weariness. I knew my husband only too well and remained silent as he peeled off his flying helmet and goggles with weary impatience and searched in his pocket for a cigarette. He lit it as we reached the lee of the mess, lines of strain and fatigue clearly etched on his face in the flare of the match.

If I voiced my fears for his safety while making a fast turn or when pulling out of a steep dive high above the clouds where the element of air in the third dimension reacts differently to our senses, he would laugh and say that I was imagining things again. The ocean of air, our vast canopy of protection, is of a different substance in the higher reaches of its secret heights. It has accelerated the tempo of transport for those who climb the sky, but the smoke and smog of humankind's poisonous habits can retard the higher functions of his brain and senses when he exists as a denizen of the ocean floor of air and must breathe a denser pressure of molecules in slower time.

As we entered the lounge-bar, the heated atmosphere caused me to choke and recoil. Cigarette smoke hung in blanketlike bands across the room. Aircraft technicians and personnel set up a monotonous hum of conversation against the discordant din of the background music. With a feeling of despair in my heart, I quickly bagged our usual table by the window. I could open it without anyone seeing and get some fresh air, no matter how cold, whenever a feeling of claustrophobia affected me.

It was bad enough being in England with a cloud blanket that never seemed to lift—days and days of it. I longed for the wide-open spaces of my homeland far away to the south, a beloved land where the east wind blows with the fresh clean tang of the sea across vast stretches of rolling grassland and the glory of the sky is open to the heavens. A land where the Southern Cross glitters with spangled arms across the meridian and the deep bowl of the sky, alight with the glow of millions of star systems. I longed to breathe the air of the wide-open spaces again, with the fragrance of rain, and to feel the wind on my face. I belonged out there, in the pure atmosphere of the sky, flying—flying over the mountains, flying through the clouds and under the glittering stars, in the velvet sky, with the glow of light always there high above. I longed to live in the ocean of air, to hear the celestial note of the wind, to sense and feel the vibrations and freedom of our planet moving with the velocity of a spaceship through the fathomless reaches of space and away from the habitat of people who swarm and crawl on her surface like slugs of the airy depths.

Looking through the window, I noticed that the low, scudding clouds had lifted. The great pile of the de Havilland buildings stood dark and gaunt against the reflection of the lights of London on the base of the cloud mass. Brilliant lights still illuminated the hangar where the boffins studied the wonder plane. Code-named TK4, perhaps it would revolutionize flying for England, enabling the nation to have a craft to defend her skies against any of the aggressive invaders who seemed to get more and more ruthless in their quest for power and world domination and who were forever devising more horrible and diabolical weapons of destruction.

To destroy one's fellow creatures and one's planet is a reflection of mass insanity. Violence and destruction are but a symbol of power for the race of humankind on Earth—vast masses of people who have barely evolved beyond savage flesh-eating murderers. They are barbarians, whose one ambition is to destroy. The way of tolerance and coexistence with all nature is not yet understood. Instead, a twisted state of mind exists, spawned by centuries of wrong thinking and living, in all social systems set up by people of Earth. Humankind of planet Earth is thereby a product of its environment.

I longed to escape from it all, but found myself bound up at the forefront of a nation's preparations for the defense of her very existence. In a world becoming more dangerous to live in, I wondered at my husband's nonchalant attitude and realized that he would think nothing of the dangers involved. His only anxiety was to shield me from them. Little did he realize how my powers of observation, instilled since childhood, could foresee the trend of human behavior. Humankind thrives on disaster, and my mind was constantly aware of the disasters to come and the dreadful perils ahead.

"OUR PLANET IS UNDER CLOSE SURVEILLANCE BY AN ALIEN BUT HIGHLY ADVANCED CIVILIZATION FROM OUTER SPACE."

Premonitions had come to me in the past and taken tangible shape in their due time, but now time was running out fast. Perhaps it would come suddenly one night, a world war triggered in the hush of night. Perhaps it would come while my husband marked a fleeting furrow through the peaceful sky to navigate his airy wanderings. What would it be like to be annihilated in a flimsy aircraft, shot down out of a beautiful summer sky with only the stars to witness the cruel calculation of man's inhumanity to man?

My husband suddenly woke up out of his reverie over a whiskey.

"We have an appointment with the Chief this evening," he said.

The evening was bitterly cold when we went out into the snow-filled atmosphere, and I was thankful the wind had dropped.

We were soon with the Chief, an old friend who greeted us warmly in his natural, courteous manner. His eyes took in every detail of our appearance, a habit of cold observation instilled through years of heavy responsibility and duty to his country. I was happy to be with him again and had much to tell him, so much to tell of a particularly thrilling nature, something of wonder and excitement that I felt sure he would understand and listen to. A man of his experience and position would know of the spaceships appearing in our skies.

"Yes, my dear," he said. "I am very anxious to hear what you have to say, and what you think. A report has just been handed to me that an unidentified flying object was sighted by two of our pilots while on a cross-country maneuver this afternoon in the vicinity of your husband's flight path with the TK4. Some time back, I received a dispatch from South Africa stating that you had both reported the sighting of an unidentified flying object, which paced your DH aircraft while flying over the Drakensberg."

His eyes softened as I looked directly into them and told him every detail of our experience, and of my childhood experiences.

"It is as I suspected," the Chief replied. "Our planet is under close surveillance by an alien, but highly advanced, civilization from outer space."

He paused for a moment, looking at me intently.

"And you, my dear, seem to be dedicated to this. You know what to look for, you are not afraid, and I can think of no one more qualified. Besides, you have intuition and imagination, which is very important in this advanced research. Will you do it for us?"

"Of course I shall do it," I answered without hesitation.

"Thank you, my dear," the Chief said. "I feel sure something will come of this. Help and guidance will be given to the sorely afflicted peoples of this planet, who seem unable to live in peace and harmony. And as you know, you have been thoroughly vetted. We know the full history of your family and its ancient lineage."

"This research may take you many years," he went on. "Therefore, every detail of information must be given to me, no matter how fantastic. We are dealing with a fantastic realization. I want you to use your powers of extrasensory perception and follow up any hunches you may have. This extraordinary ability you are so liberally endowed with can be of tremendous value to us."

The hour was very late when we left him, and in that moment of leaving, I was aware that he had slumped back in his chair. What dreadful responsibilities rested on his frail shoulders. My heart went out to him, and the memory of the deep sadness in his eyes spurred me to redouble my efforts to find the great spaceship one day, to seek help for the people of Earth—and perhaps salvation—from an advanced people from beyond our skies. I stood stunned for a moment—trapped, helpless. My natural independence of spirit—the glorious heritage of freedom I was brought up with—faded away into the mists of the past and the dead weight of responsibility threatened to crush my soul.

Early the next morning I escaped in the MG along the great north road to the village of Aston and the home of my paternal ancestors. The family seat, Astonbury, was set among the ancient trees of England, which dappled the emerald sward with leafy shadows. Leaving the MG in the drive, I walked on through the park, inhaling the fragrance of sweet, damp earth and vegetation. Fallow deer paced beside me with gentle patience, sensing my preoccupation, while through the trees the great mansion of Astonbury glowed with its wealth of rose brick and many Tudor chimneys. Gone were the halcyon days of freedom and leisure. The ease and grace of a world that belonged to the few, in which I had been born and nurtured, had faded away into the fog of time. I found solace, however, in the quiet beauty and peace of the scented park.

I looked toward the lily pond my grandmother had made out of a bomb crater many years ago when the beautiful mansion was spared from destruction and the evil thoughts of those intent upon their many tribal wars. Walking on, beside the ancient, creepered walls of my ancestral home, I resolved to help protect a freedom inherited through the centuries as only an island nation can know—the freedom of the seas, the freedom of the skies, the freedom of space. Freedom is the very stuff of life, and without it one ceases to live.

Yet I realized that most people were unaware of the wider scene of faraway places. They could not connect the whole or comprehend how it would affect them all with crushing impact in years to come. They had rallied around in panic to stem the flow of Hitler's hordes, but there was no vision to gauge the blow to England's pride that was now being forged. The veil of silence is so cunningly drawn over the perception of man that he cannot see the plan to enslave him with wars and rumors of still more wars to come—wars of racial strife, black against white—in a bid to take over the planet.

Each Year on Earth Goes by a Little Faster than the One Before.

Gazing into the limitless sky, I suddenly felt a longing so intense that it seemed to transport me away from the material things about me. It was a longing to see the great spaceship again, hovering like a wraith in the depths of blue—mysterious, unattainable and remote from this warring planet. Where was she now, and where did she come from, and why was I so deeply affected by the thought of her? Did she nurture some precious being who would change my whole life, and who was already in telepathic communication with me?

In my longing to escape from the dangerous confines of this planet, a strange restlessness filled my soul, and I sensed this urgency with acute knowledge. To go home—that was it, I thought. I must go home to the rolling foothills of the Drakensberg, where the long grasses whisper and sing to the touch of the south wind that brings the tang of the sea in its breath. Perhaps my freedom would come sooner than I expected. Perhaps I could go home to the freedom of the mountains I loved, the mountains of the Dragon hiding in the mist.

I longed to turn from the casual and flippant ways of humankind. The honor and ethics of my upbringing were deeply rooted, and I had found my only happiness in the sky. That was now denied me, as fighter planes and bombers took to the air. I was grounded and always shadowed by a lithe individual who kept his distance, as the Chief netted me within his circle of security. Perhaps I did know too much, I thought—and the first twinge of fear struck at my heart.

The only escape and refuge was Astonbury, the home of my beloved grandmother, whose gentle presence could still be felt throughout the vast mansion. Her love of horses, inherited from her ducal parents, was portrayed in unexpected places with the magic of a true artist, and I could feel her guiding hand on my shoulder as I wandered on through the garden. It seemed that my future would be shaped from here, where there was so much gentleness amidst a violent universe. Here, the old retired horses could browse away their closing days in the sheltered home paddock, and the cats could sleep in peace by the kitchen range, always sensing the presence of my lovely grandmother in the home of her ancestors.

My questing mind had searched through the years for skies and seas of sapphire blue, a land and seascape not of this world, but another home of life, another island moving in the vast void of heaven where soft mountains mantled with emerald sward sweep down to the sea. That tranquil sea of vast dimensions touched a chord in my memory like a note sounding in the key of evolution, eternally vibrating in the scale of the spectrum.

I knew of a lovely planet glowing in the velvet depths of space beyond the light barrier. My soul attuned to her eternal vibration and my destiny forever entwined within her magnetic field as the magic of the lodestone gives affinity of telepathic thought to permeate the mind. I felt sure that one day I would find this mysterious and exotic land—I never doubted its existence. It was a race memory, revealed by time as a dimension of development, as time is of our mortal essence and is steadily accelerating our consciousness toward simultaneity and the infinite. Each year on Earth goes by a little faster than the one before.

WOULD AN ADVANCED CIVILIZATION HELP US TO FIND THESE SECRETS TO INTERSTELLAR TRAVEL?

My gentle parents, far away in the sunny land of my birth, wrote to me about time and how it had speeded up for them. In aging, one's inner clock slows down while Earth time remains constant. This planet moves in three directions at the same time, giving to us our speed or flow of time—past, present and future. There is less and less time to do things as one grows older, and time is speeded up because the processes of the living body are slowing down.

As planet Earth rotates and speeds in orbit about the star of her system while the whole solar system moves in orbit about the nucleus of the galaxy, we mark intervals of time by the clock. We become slaves to it and, harassed by the continuous and inexorable ticking away of intervals of time, our souls cry out for peace and freedom from it. If we knew how, we could control the variable nature of time, as time is a wave motion in a triple unity with light and gravity. Perhaps we could find an alternating wave motion in time and escape to the stars.

I felt sure that this was already a reality for an advanced civilization out there, whose spaceships could move in a stream of time in reverse to our time. Perhaps they would help us to find these secrets to interstellar travel, if we could forge a link with them. And the link, I knew, would indeed be found—through love.

CHAPTER 3

THE SECRETS OF LIGHT

W e received transfer orders home to South Africa, and the Chief's instructions to me before leaving England still rang in my mind: "Find that spaceship at all costs. It could mean the salvation of our planet—and our race."

A shiver of apprehension caused me to catch my breath as he said these words. Our beautiful planet, host to such a destructive predator as man! It is no wonder that we lift our eyes to the heavens.

I knew that it was a spaceship from another planet, another world somewhere out there, and through the years, I had lived with this knowledge, knowing within my heart that the spaceship would return. I prepared myself spiritually, mentally and intellectually to attain a wholeness with the universe and tune in to the infinite. I worked to develop a sense of telepathic communication with all nature and living creatures and, in so doing, to become whole in spirit, mind and body. To meet with people of a highly-advanced civilization, thousands of years ahead of Earth people, I could only hope for contact if I was prepared to go halfway to find them.

Being aware of their presence in our skies, I practiced telepathy with horses, dogs and cats, and even with plants, machines or anything with the electric spark of life. I found this to be of great value in my experience through the years, and eventually I was able to communicate with the man who came in the spaceship from beyond our solar system. As time went by through the years of preparation, the telepathic link became stronger and stronger. In the understanding of universal harmony, I knew his name within my soul and I knew that he was there within the spaceship.

Upon our arrival at Cape Town, the scene through the window was dreary, windblown and wet. The rain lashed in torrents against the windows, driven by the swift downdrafts of a southeaster. Where were the open skies of my beloved homeland, the fathomless depths of blue? The fairest Cape in the world stood braced against the relentless polar front. It swept across the empty southern seas from Antarctica where a volcanic link lies in the seabed from the mighty peak of Mount Erebus to the tumbled mountains of the Cape where vineyards flourish in the valleys.

I had seen the cloud cap draped snugly upon the summit of Table Mountain, with another stay-put cloud hovering in the windy sky high above. It was strange and lovely—smooth and lens-shaped with iridescent colors around its circumference, like a painting by Dali. Its unearthly beauty was anchored by a standing wave of air that billowed up from some irregularity of ground to windward. It was an omen of bad weather and cold leaping winds, and we prepared for a day of rain squalls, with all aircraft grounded.

The shrill and demanding clamor of the telephone startled me out of my reverie, and the peace and seclusion of my office transformed to bedlam by the screeching monster. The voice at the other end of the line was strident with excitement.

"Fire! Fire in No. 11 hangar!"

My mind raced ahead, oblivious of the flow of words pouring out along the wires. All the planes were grounded, and sabotage was so easy in a land where attack was unknown and unprepared for. My husband would be there fussing round the planes by now. Slamming the receiver down, I grabbed my raincoat and ran out into the icy squall. The flames had enveloped two of the planes and my husband was valiantly pushing away another. As I ran to help him, a petrol tank exploded. We were both flung to the ground, and a black cloud smothered my senses.

I HAD FELT THE TOUCH OF DEATH AND KNEW IT WAS ALL PART OF THE PREPARATION.

Very slowly, I became aware of light and movement around me. I felt terribly hot and pushed my foot into the lovely, cold sheets at the side of the mattress. I pushed the bedclothes away and tried to turn over. A kind face framed in white linen hovered over me, and hands wrapped the hot bedclothes about me again.

I was restless and I longed for coolness. Suddenly, the heat faded away as my mind reached out for relief. A refreshing breeze fanned my cheeks, and a scene, luminous but with a clear perspective, unfolded around me. I was sitting in lush, cool emerald grass on the top of a hill overlooking an expanse of dark blue sea. The fragrant breeze blew from across the sapphire sea and, far below, a beautiful curve of bay sparkled in the morning sunlight. Behind me stretched a fantastic mass of mountains, their emerald slopes dotted with enormous golden trees and mountaintops of deep rose rocks glowing in the sunlight against the delphinium blue of sky. Coming in toward the hill from across the sea, a beautiful circular craft glinted and flashed in the sunlit atmosphere. The lovely vision faded as quickly as it had come, and I heard voices around me.

"She is out of danger now," a man said softly. "It's quite remarkable— I didn't expect her to pull through."

The familiar atmosphere of a busy hospital, the muffled sounds beyond the half-open door, flowed back with lucid adaptation. I turned my head to look out through the window and saw the wooded mountainside of Devil's Peak. Above the timberline a banner of cloud streamed like a flag, continuously gaining new substance as air, riding on the wind's back, condensed near the crest. As I slowly regained my strength, the lovely vision I had experienced remained alive and real, filling me with a warmth of secret happiness. Here was the mysterious and exotic land of my dreams, the faraway planet somewhere beyond the light barrier and the time barrier of this solar system.

I COULD SEE A MAN STANDING IN THE SHIP, LOOKING AT ME. I LOOKED BACK AT HIM WITHOUT FLINCHING.

Soon I was allowed to leave Groote Schuur hospital and go home to the rolling foothills of the Drakensberg Mountains. I had felt the touch of death and knew it was all part of the preparation. It is when one can respond with love and kindness, understanding and wisdom, and with no vestige whatsoever of fear or hate that one can hope to meet with the people who maintain the interstellar spaceships, to approach within their domain. I waited for the man from space to make physical contact, but the key was first to find him with my mind and spirit in complete harmony. It happened one stormy night while I lay quietly meditating.

The rain lashed in torrents, driven by gale force winds, across the iron roof of the farmhouse, sometimes roaring down the chimney to fan the flames of the log fire. My sister had gone to the kitchen to make tea when, suddenly, I was teleported up through the ceiling, though my body remained on the couch. As I went up through the clouds, I could feel the wind blowing in my face and pressing my cheeks inward with its reality.

Above the clouds, two spaceships were hovering in the clear sky. Akon's ship lowered a little and I knew we had found each other. This brought me into close communication—a bond of affinity and love—with Akon, who assured me of his physical presence and transmitted much information about his way of life, where he came from and the great civilization of his people. When the time was right, I went out into the mountains to find him, away from the cities and pollution of Earth people, away to the beautiful and mysterious Drakensberg of Natal where I was born in the year of Halley's Comet.

The Amazulu called to me from the mountaintops, their voices echoing through the valleys, tuning in to the grapevine of their own method of communication. They told of the great wagon of the sky and the fiery visitors from the heaven country, who would come to take me away in the lightning bird whose scales glitter in many colors. It would land in a cloud upon a hill and there would be a meeting together. The storm doctor and the witch had foretold this and the legend had grown around me since I was a child.

"The golden hair of your head will bring the *Abelungu* from the sky," they called across the valleys as I listened to their descriptive language, understanding it as well as my own. "You are 'one who brings together,' *Inkosazana*! The heaven dwellers will come and take you away from us." And the song spread away in the hills.

It was at this time that the spaceship came, and I sensed her proximity as great white cumulus clouds sailed with the east wind across the sky, clearcut against the blue, using the clouds as camouflage. She tested my patience and faith, and she knew the secret within my soul.

Gazing into the depths of blue, I saw a flash of light against the sky and then again near the outline of a cloud. The great spaceship appeared then, hovering below the clouds. It moved rapidly toward the hilltop, slipping gracefully and soundlessly through the air to hover again, a few hundred meters above and to the south of the hilltop. Then it slowly lost height to remain about a meter from the ground.

A pulsating hum filled the air that caused my eardrums to pop from the sudden displacement of air caused by the huge ship. Its circular hull was at least 18 meters in diameter, with a rounded dome in the middle and three large portholes facing me, through which I could see a man standing in the ship, looking at me.

I looked back at him without flinching. He stood there with his arms folded across his chest, regarding me with a compelling and hypnotic attraction about his eyes that seemed to influence and control me, even at that distance. With a shock, I realized that I was entirely forgetting my training and powers of observation and it was with great willpower that I looked away from his eyes. I studied his face—the most wonderful face I had ever seen—and I felt a sense of affinity and love.

A slight smile softened the ascetic lines of his face. It was a gentle smile and it caused my heart to miss a beat. I knew that smile had softened his eyes too, and I dared not look again into those eyes. My heart beat against my ribs with suffocating intensity; I felt faint. A man from another planet, another world, influencing my life! Time seemed to stand still at that moment. There was no fear. There was only a deep and exciting happiness.

HE INSTANTLY ANSWERED MY THOUGHTS.

I observed his spaceship. Although I could see through the port-hole, the whole effect was a dazzling brightness from its smooth glass-like surface—a bright haziness that came from the ship itself and not from the Sun shining on it. Watching the hull, I realized it was spinning rapidly in a clockwise motion while the rounded dome remained stationary. It lowered a little more toward the ground, and the brightness began to hurt my eyes. The top of my head ached from the vibrations set up in the atmosphere, and I wondered how much longer I could stand the pain in my head from these pulsing vibrations without turning away and running.

Akon

The spaceship slowly began to rise vertically, the smooth perfection of its compact design etched against the blue sky through a haze of the white mist surrounding it. Then, suddenly, it flashed into the depths of blue and was gone, and only a heat-wave effect shimmered in the atmosphere where seconds before it had hovered. My hat sailed up into the air like a live thing, and a blast of hot air struck me. My hat had gone as if there was no gravity to bring it back, and a strange feeling of weightlessness caused me to sit down suddenly on the grass.

I remained sitting, close to the Earth, too nervous to stand up again. To the west, the clouds had moved away from the vast profile of Giant's Castle and the sleeping face was outlined against the blue sky. The immense bulk of the sleeping giant stretched away to Cathkin and beyond and to the jagged teeth of Mont-aux-Sources where clouds swirled up from its base.

Breathing in the pure atmosphere of the mountain, filled with a harmony unknown anywhere else in the world, I regained my composure and quietly sat and thought about it all. It was no good reproaching myself for failing the first time. I knew there would be another. I would be ready to meet him then. I knew it was necessary to gain still more knowledge and instruction from him through telepathy, to relax and understand the presence of his faster-than-light spaceship, and thereby to go with him.

I closed my eyes and sighed deeply in complete happiness. As I did so, I could see his compelling eyes again, willing me to be aware of his presence always, controlling my thoughts and actions. A sense of fulfillment and a deep and everlasting love filled my heart for the man in the spaceship. There was no doubt in my mind that he would return—and soon.

The months went by, and there was no further sign of the spaceship and the man who maintained it. Over the vast and majestic mountains of the Dragon, the Amazulu quietly went about their work in hushed and awed silence—waiting, waiting.

Then one morning I awoke early and knew that he was coming back. I looked through the window into the depths of blue and again sensed the pull of the unknown—the deep and strong call of something beyond the skies of Earth. My heart answered the magnetic pull that touched my mind. The vibration came gently out of the mysterious sky with the south wind, with the tang of the sea wind as it rustled and rippled through the long grasses of the hills—the cool sea wind bearing the fragrance of mist, a finer entity of minute moisture cells sweeping up over the mountains. This fragrance that I had known and loved through the years now filled my being with a sudden longing to return.

The author, standing on the spot where the spaceship landed.

Hurrying into my clothes, I set out for the hilltop. It was a long walk from the farm homestead, and the fresh mountain breeze flapped the damp pleats of my kilt against my knees. I felt cold as the summit of Flying Saucer Hill loomed higher and the going became more arduous. I climbed the steep incline to the top where I saw the silver spaceship resting on the ground in the bowl at the top of the hill.

Beside it stood a tall man. I looked at him with awe, and I could feel my beating heart. In that wonderful moment I didn't hesitate, but ran down the rough slope, straight to the man beside his ship. Within seconds I was at his side. Laughing gaily, he caught me round the waist and swung me up on to the hull of his ship. We both laughed as though it was the most natural thing in the world. Then he spoke to me in precise English and his voice was like a caress.

"Not afraid this time?"

Holding me close in his arms, he smiled gently as I looked up into his kind gray eyes.

"I have known your face within my heart all my life," I answered.

"I am not from any place on this planet called Earth," he whispered with his lips in my hair.

He carried me into the cabin of his spaceship and set me down on a soft, circular bench. Another man sat at a control panel. He looked up, and a smile of welcome lit his handsome face. I saw the door closing from between double walls. Without a sound it shut automatically. The shiny wall and door seemed to fuse, and no opening remained.

I inhaled sharply. The shiny, circular walls of the cabin were sealed. Covers closed over the portholes with a sudden movement, and there was no trace left of them either—there were just the smooth walls, illuminated with a soft glowing light as natural as daylight on the surface of a planet. The whole cabin was lit with this soft, reflected light. The effect of it was light without shadows, and I saw no wiring or cables. Fresh, invigorating air filled the cabin and I breathed in a higher oxygen content, immediately feeling the benefit from it. A gentle humming sound came from the ship, accompanied by a slight vibration. There was no sense of movement, but I knew we were rising slowly into the air. In that moment of wonder, I glanced at the pilot, who sat at a simple control panel composed of pushbuttons.

The smooth simplicity of the spaceship took my breath away. The floor was covered with a beautiful rose-red type of carpeting, soft and springy yet very firm. It covered the whole of the cabin floor, encircling a bubble-like lens in the center of the cabin. The bench I was sitting on was extremely comfortable and set low to the floor. Another half-moon bench faced the lens on the other side. The lens itself was like a crystal bubble, only half of it showing above the floor, with a circlet of shining gold set in pearl around its base.

The tall man sat beside me and held my hand in both of his hands. The firm warmth and reassurance of his touch caused me to relax completely, and I leaned back against the soft bench.

"My name is Akon," he said. "I am a scientist, and my research takes me to many planets beyond our home system. Sheron, who greeted you as we came in, is my pilot, and he is also a scientist. Our home system is beyond—far beyond—this small star with its family of planets. We come from a double star system."

With wonder, I looked into his eyes—those fantastic, compelling eyes. He smiled at me in his gentle way, and then his whole face lit up for a fleeting moment. I was fascinated by his strong and fine appearance, tall and strikingly handsome with a force of character unknown to me. His ascetic face was grave but tender, and his golden hair shone white at the temples as he moved his head to glance at the viewing lens. It was a most striking face, with aquiline features, high cheekbones and light gray eyes slanting up to the temples. His forehead was high and his skin golden and fair, with no vestige of suntan. There were humor lines around his eyes and deep lines down his cheeks. He was an older man, well past middle age, with a strong and lithe body just under two meters in height.

His hair was straight and long, behind his ears and to the nape of the neck, and he wore a plain, close-fitting garment that shimmered with a silvery sheen. It was all one piece, light and comfortable like a shiny nylon, and very soft. The trousers narrowed down to the ankles and covered his feet like a soft glove on which he walked. Long sleeves closed tightly around his wrists, and a high round neckline fitted him like a polo-neck sweater. Only his hands, face and head were exposed, and I noticed gloves and a head covering of the same shiny material lying on the other bench. The head covering looked tight-fitting and had slits for the eyes slanting upward and slits for the mouth and nose.

Longing to cast off the formality of my English upbringing, I tried hard to stifle my natural reserve. Here was a man immune to any artificial or feigned approach to human relationships.

He instantly answered my thoughts.

"I would not have you otherwise. I love you as you are. You are now one of us."

A deep emotion and great happiness spread its warmth through my mind and body. The wondrous reality was almost too much for me, and I could not find words adequate to express the fullness of love within my heart for this man from another planet.

"I KNOW WHAT IS BEST FOR YOU AND WILL ALWAYS LOOK AFTER YOU, MY BELOVED."

"My beloved," he whispered. "There is no need for you to say anything. I know everything—I have observed you before. It is a knowledge and understanding that we share, and you now belong to me. It was only necessary for me to wait until you had grown up in this knowledge and understanding. To be one of us, you must think as we do. I observed you first when you were a child, with your sister in the garden of your home in the valley adjoining the hill. At other times, I have watched you growing up, flying through the skies of Earth looking for me, and I watched while the lightning high in the sky wrapped you with its purifying flame to make you mine."

"It has been a lifetime for me," I whispered back.

"Your delicate face is still filled with wonder and awe," he answered.

Gathering me into his arms, he kissed me on the lips. A magical, electric current seemed to fuse us together in an eternity of ecstasy. In that moment, I knew that the art of love was of the mind and soul, not only of the body.

Smiling at my thoughts, he put his hand gently under my chin, tilting my head back and looking deep into my eyes.

"We rarely mate with Earth women," he said. "When we do, we keep the offspring to strengthen our race and infuse new blood."

Trembling with excitement, my sensitive being responded to the beauty of his love. My soul was enraptured by his nearness and spellbound by his eyes, his gentle but compelling eyes. The viewing lens suddenly flashed on, and the magic spell was broken.

Akon's golden hair shone white at the temples as he moved his head to glance again at the lens, a smile creasing still more the deep lines down his cheeks. Bending forward, he pressed a button set in the circlet of gold about the base of the lens. The shiny walls and ceiling of the spaceship changed to sapphire blue like the skies of my dreams, and I got the impression of being out of the spaceship and looking at a panorama in all directions. The wonderful panorama unfolded all around and in every direction—all around the horizon of Earth and beyond, into the far distances of the sky.

My hand tightened around Akon's, and he took my other hand and drew me closer. I saw the Drakensberg range to the west and the line of blue sea to the southeast. My eyes wide with wonder, I watched surface features flatten and merge into a uniform color scheme of browns, greens and bluish haze. Away to the north, clouds covered the surface, the tops shining white in the sunlight with dark shadows beneath. The empty, sky-swept country spread out—the real magic carpet of Earth herself, her magic revealed beyond ancient ken. Her roundness became apparent, her mysteries uncovered to the all-seeing eye from the far reaches of the sky.

The seas appeared as a wide expanse of darkness against the lighter land masses, which became curved against the darkness of the sky. A brilliant blue band hugged the Earth along the horizon like the deep blue wavelength of the primary rainbow. From the outermost skirts of the sky a hazy, faint reflection from the envelope of air that wraps the planet in onion-like layers etched the shores of Africa against the sea, except where clouds shone white.

Earth showed her veiled face to us, floating in space, her delicate blueness lightly shrouded in white clouds swirling in wind patterns. She rotated smoothly, her rounded sides moving over. The polar caps glistened white, the southern polar region large and pronounced and the northern cap smaller but with a beauty of shifting pulsating colors like a banner reaching into space. Her bulging waistline rotated about her flattened poles like a fat apple with a heavy base. The enormous power and energy of her being filled the whole viewing lens, her night side moving over into the sun side in a slow smooth rotation.

A lovely shifting display of colors in the ionosphere emanated from the auroral zones. It formed a rainbow effect over the magnetic polar regions, giving the Earth delicate veiled banners that reached out into space. These mingled with remnants of her atmosphere, which were left behind in the velocity of her orbit around the Sun to form a tenuous tail, tapered to a leeward point by the solar wind.

We moved away into a blue darkness like the shadow of the Earth that catches up at the end of day. The walls and ceiling of the spaceship changed color, and the many-hued stars shone with a brilliance of light. I felt an overwhelming sense of remoteness as I watched the distant sphere of Earth—a blue and white globe, a home of life, an island moving in the vast void of heaven.

Would I be allowed to return to my family there on that distant planet? My children there were still young, and my mind became troubled.

"There is no need to be nervous," Akon reassured me as he held me closer. "We are proceeding to our mothership, where you will be our guest for a short period before we escort you back to the hill on which we found you. I know what is best for you and will always look after you, my beloved."

I had known the truth of it in my heart long before hearing it from his own lips, when in years gone by I had gazed into the depths of blue with a longing I could not then define. Now I knew the reason for my longing and why my whole being had always been aware of someone, of an affinity of souls and a love to be fulfilled with wondrous anticipation and awe. I knew now that, through the years, he had prepared my mind for this eternal love, this love of a man and a woman.

"THE KEY TO ALL LIFE AND THE UNIVERSE LIES IN THE HARMONIC INTERACTION OF LIGHT."

At that distance from Earth, my mind became aware of a new dimension. Humans there—with all their petty quarrels, cruelty and vicious occupancy of all their bits of territory—ceased to exist. Gone were the insular and selfish ways of human beings on Earth, their fecundity destroying the beauty of their planet like parasites swarming over her surface. The mother planet harbored life on her surface and within her surface. She protected it against the radiations of space and provided it with abundance, yet she shielded a viper within her bosom.

My mind was full of questions, but checking the impulse, I looked around the circular cabin, noticing the simplicity and beauty of design, the comfort and sense of security. There was a simple row of pushbuttons on a panel for flight control and robot control, as well as television far in advance of anything we know, telescopes and searchlights of immense power and range, remote-controlled scanning disks and television eyes.

A map of our galaxy, the Milky Way, filled the domed ceiling. We saw its polar view, rotating slowly in its distant velocity of majestic movement. Its seven closely wound, dust-streaked spiral arms glowed blue with the light of young, massive stars. Millions of stars gleamed around the hub or nucleus, lighting up the clouds of hydrogen gas with the divine colors of the spectrum and the overcast of rose-red halo stars. A flashing light pinpointed our position in the Sun's system, far out on a limb. I gasped in wonder as I looked up at this stupendous, lens-shaped galaxy of ours—a supersystem riding like a glowing wheel in the remote void—where before the domed ceiling had appeared as a sky of sapphire blue.

A misty shape began to emerge in the great bubble lens and I saw the mothership suspended like a planet in the velvet void. The radiations from the Sun cast a sheet of white light on her enormous side, while her shadow side glowed with an ashen light like a planet taking her environment with her. Her radiant energy propulsion glowed around her in the visible wavelengths of blue and violet.

Again my mind filled with questions and this time I could not contain them.

"Have you been out into intergalactic space?"

"We will need to perfect our spaceships still more for a voyage of that nature," Akon said. "We are now preparing for it, enlarging our scientific survey ships like this one. As you have noticed, this ship is shaped like a galaxy, and once we have perfected the larger spaceships, which vary in diameter, we will be able to move through intergalactic space. Our intergalactic ship is exactly twice the diameter of this one, or twice the harmonic, and we are creating still larger spaceships for interstellar and intergalactic vibratory changes in the unified field. Circular ships of this type are a duplication of nature—they take their environment with them like a natural celestial object."

"How are these spaceships created?" I asked. "They are not just constructed in a building yard, then?"

"No, not on the surface of a planet. Our spaceships are created by converting pure energy into physical substance, and we do this in space. The material of the spaceship's outer skin is completely smooth, without rivets—the material is created in one piece in a continuously circular smooth shape. The radius of the curvature transforms the total mass of the spaceship's outer skin into a combination of matter and antimatter, as the atomic creation of the outer skin is conducive to energizing in alternate pulses. This is achieved when the entire system is switched on, by pressing that red button on the panel. A unified field of light instantly encircles the spaceship—an electrogravitic field that acts on all parts simultaneously, including the atoms of one's body.

"These field differentials interact to create a vacuum that encircles the spaceship, and it shifts without the restriction of speed and without sound in the atmosphere of a planet. The light emanating from the ship is subject to varying time and gravitic waves, either shortened or lengthened. All radiations and molecules are pushed aside in varying speeds and quantities to emit light, and the difference in speeds is perceived by the eye as colors.

"These micro-atoms of light form an electrostatic shield around this interstellar survey ship, this ship of light. A light-thrust of three beams controls and directs its maneuverability in harmonic interaction. The whole is a combination of cosmic forces—electric, magnetic, tempic and resonating. It is the harmonic interaction of the four forces of the universe—the unified field. Like a natural celestial object, this ship protects her crew as a planet would, taking its environment with it through the fathomless reaches of space.

"The tempic field, or time field, is the controlling field. It maneuvers the spaceship from one time field to another within the vibration of a higher frequency that emanates from the total mass of the ship's triple skin. As the field intensifies, the spaceship becomes invisible to any watcher on the surface of Earth. It disappears completely or suddenly appears again. It can vanish on the spot when landed or it can materialize again. On Earth, the first indication of this would be a heat-wave effect during daylight in the atmosphere. At other times, depending on atmospheric conditions, the molecules of atmosphere surrounding the area of proximity to the spaceship condense into a cloud as it comes into the condensation level of the atmosphere. This can occur while it is hovering or moving in the sky, whether the ship is visible through the cloud or in its invisible state. All you can see, usually, is an inorganic cloud that sometimes builds and bubbles up into a vast organic cumulonimbus, spreading storm destruction far and wide or simply decaying away slowly in the higher atmosphere."

Akon thought for a few moments and continued.

"The minimum temperature around the spaceship allows her complete mobility and velocity without limits of stress, strain, heating or restrictive influence of atmospheric pressure. This gives us feather-light landings, in a state of weightlessness, on any surface of the planet. The heat blast that is felt in the proximity of the spaceship is caused by the sudden air displacement. Micro-atoms of light are stopped, and are thereby equal to heat. These micro-atoms are pushed aside by the field differentials surrounding the spaceship, which spins faster than the speed of sound, accounting for the lack of noise.

"This shield prevents all fauna from approaching too close to the spaceship and prevents aircraft from moving into the fringes of the vortex where they would be affected by this area of reduced binding and simply fall apart in the air. That has happened at times in the past. We worked out the design of this spaceship in mathematical synchronization. It steps up the frequency interaction of light within the unified field, which permeates all of existence, making it possible for a shift in space-time to occur.

"The road to the stars unfolds within a spaceship of beauty and simplicity. It generates its light from the cosmic plasma of eternity, never faltering. It is always alive and pulsating, shaped like a galaxy with a halo surrounding it and the shock wave glowing. All of creation is light, which is the key to the universe. The whole of existence—throughout the planetary systems, the stars and the depths of interstellar space—is made up of visible and invisible waves of light. To the seen and unseen—to all energy, substance, liquids, gases and all life—the release of micro-atoms of light from oxygen is the source of all life. The electromagnetic waveform, or light, forms the building blocks of the cosmos in which we have our being, as micro-atoms of light in greater unities are equal to atoms.

"Mental forces, spiritual strength, soul attainment and thoughts are all made up of micro-atoms of different speeds in the wavelength of light. Electricity is comprised of micro-atoms of light, and while sound and color occur when the micro-atoms have different speeds. When micro-atoms are stopped, they create heat. Light is an intelligent energy that can be thought into existence and substance. The pattern of the micro-atoms of light alters with changing thoughts when one achieves the formula for the harmonic vibration of light. The key to all life and the universe lies in the harmonic interaction of light.

"A mathematical formula for all transportation lies in the vibratory frequencies of the light harmonic, with antigravity waves and time waves—which are simply the frequency rate between each pulse of the spiral of light. By controlling this frequency rate, the flow of time can be varied, and one simply moves within one's environment, within the protection of the spaceship, instantaneously from one planet to another, or one solar system to another. Time, as a geometric, is controlled or eliminated."

"And the speed of light, is that also a geometric?" I asked.

"We speak of the measure of light, not of the speed of light. Light gives the illusion of velocity, when in reality it is a pulse resonating in the frequencies of time and gravity. Thereby, our galaxy is created to the universal geometric harmonics of light—light is a universal geometric. Time and gravity, or a reversal in the flow of time and antigravity, can be achieved by altering the energy of light pulsing through space, through the atmosphere of planets, and throughout all creation, as micro-atoms of light form the atoms of all gases, liquids and solids.

"As I mentioned before, the unified differentials of light interact to create a vacuum encircling the spaceship, and it moves without sound or the restriction of speed as the molecules of atmosphere are pushed aside instead of piling up in flight. In space, the unified field of light creates a shift in space and time. No velocity is involved—there is only a shift in frequency as the spaceship vibrates in harmonic resonance to interact with the wave energy of light pulsing throughout the galaxy. It simply uses the fabric of space itself, which is light, vibrating in waveform frequencies in alternate pulses of matter and antimatter. Thereby we overcome the problems of space travel beyond the light barrier.

"Earth scientists still have the restriction of the sound barrier in atmospheric flight. Perhaps they will discover that there is no restriction that causes the sonic boom if they can perfect an aircraft that pushes aside the molecules of air instead of allowing the molecules to pile up against the craft."

"Like the tunnel or ionized path that lightning creates and uses as a channel through the air from ground to cloud?" I asked. I was so very interested—I could not miss one word of Akon's information.

"My beloved," he answered with a smile, "it can be a duplication of nature. If we can find all the answers to atmospheric and space travel within the simplicity of nature, so could humankind of Earth find these answers, provided they cooperate with nature instead of attempting to destroy her. The key to all this lies in harmony—harmonic interaction with all things and nature throughout our galaxy—and it is for human-kind to achieve all this first. We simply disappear with our spaceship out of this planet's time field and appear in the time field geometric of our home planet, within a neighboring solar system. You, my beloved, will simply come with us in a future time cycle."

"Is this why I could sense the spaceship moving slowly from Earth?" I asked. "Because it is necessary for me first to adapt to a slow smooth change from one time dimension to another?"

"It is not necessary, because you move within the atmosphere of the spaceship," Akon explained. "You are protected within your own environment. But we did not wish to frighten you, beloved. In future times you will feel the spaceship suddenly vibrate, a vibration from outside the sealed cabins, something apart from the ship itself. This happens when it moves in instantaneous anti-light harmonics, stepping up the frequency interaction of light (speed of light) when a shift in space-time occurs. I retained your mind though, on moving with the spaceship into this time dimension, which has enabled you to shift in complete harmony. Otherwise it would not have been possible for you to become a part of the shift in space-time beyond the light barrier, owing to the very high frequency vibration of light. We double the harmonic of light to obtain antigravitational and anti-light fields—the unified field equation that is the key to space travel or movement in space-time."

I smiled in reply.

"No wonder it has been almost a lifetime before you contacted me physically," I said.

I was suddenly thankful and very humble for my years of training and self-discipline, instilled since childhood, which now enabled me to understand completely within my mind the intricate secrets of light, and how the spaceship created this cosmic energy to use itself as a source of infinite power.

"Indeed, my beloved, misunderstanding leads to disharmony in thought forces, and I could not have taken you with me from Earth," Akon said, replying to my thoughts. "Harmony is the key to manipulating this cosmic energy, the source of all existence and matter—and thoughts.

"In their search for truth, humans of planet Earth will find that reality conforms to a mental conception. Thus, the idea of using light or gravity as a means of propulsion for spaceships not only becomes conceivable but also perceptible through mental processes.

"Yet the true nature of reality remains quite beyond their comprehension, except in brief moments of transfiguration when the soul transmits the reality or truth to the mind. Evidence for the immortality of the soul is found in this way, independent of reason, where we find the magic lease we sense as life—all made out of stardust. And the harmonic interaction of love . . . "

"PEOPLE ON EARTH USE COSMIC ENERGY, OR LIGHT, FOR DESTRUCTIVE PURPOSES."

There is always a reason for things happening in the way they do, I thought. One cannot expect everything to be handed over on a plate if one has not the requisites of knowledge, understanding, harmony, love and discipline without fear. Akon's advanced civilization cannot, at any time, become embroiled in the ruthless politics of Earth's nations. Their entire civilization and the energy source in the harmonic frequency of light depends entirely on universal harmony. Otherwise, all they have attained could fall away in explosive violence and destruction. The holy secrets of nature cannot be misused, and Akon's civilization is the guardian of these secrets. They have full awareness of their cosmic origin and affinity with nature.

Man's inhumanity to man must cease before these holy secrets of nature can be revealed for the benefit of all humanity on Earth, for the benefit of all fauna and flora. Only then will humanity achieve the destiny of all nations and peoples—to attain wholeness and harmony with the universe, and to become one with the great interstellar human family. But expansion of thought will only come in the wavelength of time when the insight of humans has reached a deeper and more spiritual level.

"What wonderful thoughts can be created for the benefit of a planet!" I said.

"Yes, my dear, they can, but only by the right people. In the hands of wrong people and politics, thoughts and words can be put into the minds of others, simply with the biological effects of low-level microwave radiation. This is completely foreign to us," Akon said sternly. "In fact, it is the opposite of what we do. We use our own minds as a source of effective

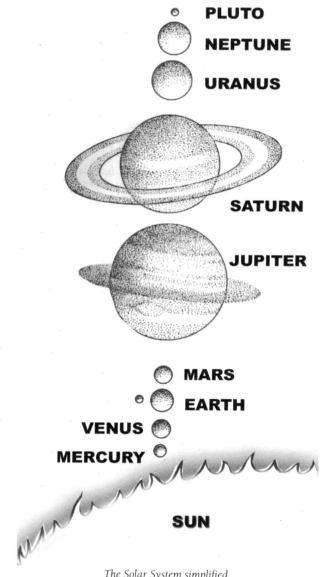

The Solar System simplified.

radiation to communicate with others. Telepathy, in other words, as you have already experienced.

"People on Earth use cosmic energy, or light, for destructive purposes. Radio wave propagation, nuclear bombs and nuclear power stations—all these are used in the wrong way. People have not the intelligence or the savvy to understand cosmic energy. And this is why we keep apart and away from people of Earth, for we shall never share the secrets of light with them.

"The electromagnetic waveform—or light—is the unified field of matter and antimatter throughout the universe," Akon explained, turning back to watch the viewing lens as we approached the great mothership. "We move within the protection of our spaceship as she alters the wavelength of light to create a shift in space and time for movement from one point or place to another."

CHAPTER 4

AN ESCAPE ROUTE TO THE STARS

"Now, as we approach the mothership," Akon continued, "you will understand how she generates the unified field. I have just been generalizing to give you a picture of the method we use, which is a duplication of nature, and therefore safe. You will know far more later, of course, even about the formula we use to generate the unified field for space journeys and how we control electricity and gravity through light for the benefit of our civilization.

"Humankind, although highly adaptable, cannot exist in space without the time cycle and atmospheric pressure in which they have evolved. A spaceship of this nature generates all these things for us in a manner similar to our home planet. The mothership is not at all suitable for travel through the intergalactic void—the shape is wrong—but since they never wear out, we will continue to use them for travel in the home galaxy."

"How can a large spaceship like this one enter the mothership?" I asked.

"This type of spaceship has no need for a carrier. We attach it to the larger vessel. It instantly bonds with a projected entrance, and we simply walk through. The smaller craft, which are used solely for planetary exploration, move into the mothership through a series of air locks, where they are carried in large hangars."

"Then you are quite independent?"

"Yes. This is my ship. I can move from one planet to another, land if I wish, or travel to other solar systems. My ship is equipped with all necessities and, as a scientific survey vehicle, is quite independent of any larger vessel. I am a scientist and my work takes me to many planets and solar systems."

"I know. Am I to be scientifically examined too?"

"My dear—enough," Akon said gently, and gathered me up in his arms. He turned to a section of the circular wall and approached it. A door slid open, through which I saw the brilliantly lit interior of the mothership. He carried me through and then put me down, keeping his arm around my waist as if I were captured booty. People clustered around us, and a young woman spoke in perfect English.

"She has slant eyes and golden hair," the woman said. "She is descended from our original stock left behind on Earth, so it is right for her to be here with us now."

They chatted with us for a while, until one of them addressed Akon in a language that sounded not unlike Latin. Then, gathering me up again, Akon carried me away from the gay crowd and up several stairways. I noticed lifts from the lower deck, but the low gradient and deep comfort of the stairs required no effort at all to climb. We were laughing together as we reached the top, where we found the commander coming to meet us. He smiled and gave a slight bow. As Akon put me down, he came forward and kissed me on both cheeks.

"Welcome, my dear," he said. "I am Akon's brother."

Stepping aside, he motioned us into a spacious room whose beauty and comfort caused me to catch my breath again. It had the same soft, glowing illumination and fresh air, and gave one the sense and feeling of being outdoors on a beautiful day. The sapphire walls and ceiling gave an impression of a depth of sky, and flowers and brilliant green plants grew in white caskets. Exotic trees cast soft shadows on luxurious divans covered in shimmering rose silks, and the entire floor was covered in a wealth of soft blue grass.

"Is it real?" I asked in amazement.

"Of course it is." Akon laughed as he lifted me up like a feather and placed me on one of the divans. As I sank into its firm comfort, I realized how exhausted I had become with all the intense excitement.

"We shall now have some refreshment. You are very tired, my beloved, and in need of the correct sustenance," Akon observed.

I looked at Akon and the commander. The tall brothers were very alike. Both had the ascetic features of an ancient race, and bore the graceful dignity and joyful relaxation of centuries of good breeding and right thinking and living. Both were wearing the same type of plain uniform, designed for comfort and air circulation, made out of a very thin material and fitting like a second skin.

Questions again trembled on my lips, but I checked the impulse for the moment, knowing that it was inopportune. Akon knew my thoughts, and his slanted eyes glanced down at me with tender possession. Talk and the incessant chatter of voices was not their way. The quiet relaxation of mental telepathy was their mode of communication.

With a sigh, I relaxed back on the soft but firm divan, stretching my limbs out in an ecstasy of delicious comfort. There was complete peace and quiet, with not even a murmur from the vast spaceship! I felt out of place, however, in my heavy Earth-type clothes. I sat up quickly, slipped my shoes off and placed them on the fresh grass. The divan was low to the floor and I could put my hand into the cool, moist blue grass. Its fragrance wafted up into my face. I wished that I could get out of my clothes and change into something more suitable.

"As We Think and Live, So the Universe Responds to Us."

A golden tray laden with delicious salads and fruits appeared, literally materializing onto the white table beside the divan, along with long-stemmed crystal containers in which golden fruit juice sparkled.

"The light ray placed it there for you," Akon said with a smile. "You had better have some of that sustenance before I answer your questions."

I wondered about that wonderful light ray. I had felt its fleeting warmth as the tray of food appeared.

The fruit juice was simply lovely, with a flavor of ripe pomegranates. The salads consisted of delicate, bright green leaves and various cut vegetables mixed with crisp nuts, flavored with almonds and spices with a creamy dressing sprinkled over. Crisp, juicy fruits like large apricots and thin slices of moist, fresh oat bread completed the most delicious meal I had ever had.

"We assimilate all the protein and vitamins we need from this diet," Akon's brother told me. "There is no need to get it secondhand through animal meat, as people of Earth do. It is all grown here in the space-ship. Therefore, it is always fresh. It is natural for you to enjoy this type of food. Your body craves it after the heavy, cooked meals prepared on Earth, which you must not touch again."

"Please tell me your name," I said. "And how is it that you are so well-acquainted with the customs, manners and language of Earth people?"

"My name is Haben," he replied, "and it is all quite simple. We have observed Earth for eons of her time. Look into our electric mirage, my dear. Then you will understand."

Beside the gold tray was a casket, shimmering with the iridescence of mother-of-pearl. Opening it, Haben selected a tiny, shimmering roll of the same material. He went to the wall, where he fitted it to a groove. Instantly, a scene in color appeared in a curtain of minute detail across the spacious room, showing the everyday happenings in part of a city on Earth.

"Why," I exclaimed, "It's Durban! The Marine Parade in perfect detail. The sea and the people—even the rickshaw boys, in all their fin-ery, showing in minute detail. And I can hear what they are saying to each other! No wonder you know all about the peoples of Earth."

The scene had materialized like a great curtain in front of us, in color with movement and sound. The molecules of air were electrified and acti-vated to reflect the scene and portray it before us as if we were standing on that very spot ourselves, instead of thousands of miles away in space. I put my hand out to touch the nearest rickshaw boy, a tall Zulu clad in brightly colored finery with oxtails hanging from a beaded band around his legs just below the knees and dried seed pods tied about his ankles. They rattled as he pranced within the shafts of his carriage.

"I'm the finest!" he called to his companions. "People will come to me first! I have more strength than any of you!"

A tingling sensation enveloped my arm as it passed through the image. The magic of the scene remained intact as two people walked between the tall Zulu and me to board his rickshaw. I was fascinated and enthralled.

Haben removed the roll and the scene faded to nothing, and the length of the luxurious room lay before my astonished gaze once more.

"I first saw you by means of this electric mirage, as we call it," Haben said. "You were sitting on the mountaintop. I was observing the southern portion of Africa at the time. Akon was with me. He told me how he had observed you as a child, your delicate face a study in wonder and awe as you watched his spaceship slowly cross the sky. We have watched you at other times as you were growing up. You are no stranger to me, my dear."

"Is this why you are now educating me to your way of life?"

"Yes, my dear." Haben said softly. "You are now one of us, and we have chosen you to mate with Akon. Our gentle race is in need of new blood to perpetuate its strength throughout the home galaxy."

Akon was watching me. I knew he was reading my thoughts as I looked into his eyes—those wonderful, gentle gray eyes that held me spellbound. I went to him, and he folded me in his arms and held me close—so close. Where, in all my long years and travels on Earth, had I ever seen such a man as he?

With my face against his chest, I asked, "Is it true that the surface of the home planet is mainly covered by seas of sapphire blue reflected from a dark blue sky, with emerald isles scattered over the seas, their mountaintops glowing rose red in the sunlight and the soft green hills sweeping down to the sea?"

"We shall show you the home planet shortly, in the electric mirage, and you will see, my beloved, how correct your knowledge is. This knowledge is within you. You were born with it—a race memory retained in time to bring us together within the magnetic fold of the universe. As we think and live, so the universe responds to us as we are within ourselves. It is an attitude of mind, a way of life, a gentle way of life from which we are born."

This wondrous truth silenced my heart to a glorious tranquillity. I was not alien—I belonged.

Akon held me closer.

"Love is a force," he whispered, "a being that needs understanding. Love is the electric force of life, the very breath and essence of life. Love is the flame of eternal beauty. Love is wonderful, and by love, one achieves supreme happiness. People who cannot love become spiritually and physically ill. Not for them the riches of the soul. They live contrary to its laws, thereby misunderstanding the true meaning of love and how it is food and life to the soul.

"Love needs to manifest within, to radiate outward, encompassing all within its radiating field as the star of our system encircles the inner planets within its vast corona. To love all things is to enfold oneself within this magnetic field of positive existence, to commune and become one with nature and live in harmony with the universe. One is alerted to the pulse of life and answers stream into the brain, telling us what to do and how to live. Once we are attuned to the pulse of light, or life, we move in harmonic rhythm with our galaxy and universe, and there is no need for hate and dissension. People on Earth do not understand this, and the fair lands of Earth are swept by the mass insanity of its peoples.

"As a physicist, I explore how nature behaves, and in this way we find the answers to our environment and are able to duplicate that environment within our spaceships. We let nature work for us and enjoy the beauty and comfort she provides without upsetting the balance and harmony of the environment. Our home planet is retained in this way. The environment and overall climate are equable and beneficial to our health.

"People of Earth need to go forward, and not to look back and live in their past. Otherwise they will not survive. We understand nature and our environment, and we avoid her ruthless violence and destruction. We counteract or anticipate her moods and observe very closely the behavior of stars and planets, as it is the stars in solar systems that control and affect the climates of planets. We understand and know well the cosmos in which we all have our being.

"The average human being on Earth does not live long enough to attain great understanding and wisdom. Ignorance and fear still remain— the fear from which hate and wars breed. It is your environment that breeds the impassive cruelty that manifests itself in human nature. Mankind's ego has always been bolstered up with the idea that his must be the only advanced and civilized race in the galaxy. Now, the realization that a race from afar perfected space travel eons ago comes as a great shock, striking at the very roots and foundations of the narrow and orthodox teachings of humankind on Earth.

"Humankind is a creature of space. Humanity is a space race, living on a planet in orbit around a star as others are also doing. Mankind is not unique, as he so fondly imagines. He believes in his singular creation with a credence that is quite fantastic, but he is merely a part of the vast interstellar human family bred and nurtured by us through the eons of time on planets in different solar systems throughout the galaxy. The level of civilization of races and peoples can only be measured by their degree of compassion.

"People of Earth can no longer be bound to the surface of their planet like creatures of two dimensions crawling about the length and breadth of their domain. They will now soar into the third dimension, height. They will see themselves as they really are, for adjustments will have to be made to their way of thinking and living before understanding and control of their environment can take place. This is of paramount importance for their advancement and for their continuing existence.

"If they do not change for the better, they will destroy themselves, and we will have no alternative but to destroy their planet to retain the harmonic balance within the Sun's system. Fair lands have been destroyed by humankind in the Sun's solar system in the past. Whole planets have been laid bare and ravaged by their destructive ways."

"Is that what happened to Mars?" I interrupted.

"Indeed, yes. Our forebears who remained within the Sun's system were not able to advance as we have been able to do. This is purely environmental. The Sun is a variable star, and the planets are subjected to epochs of change, thereby creating vast setbacks for advancing civilizations. We will now tell you about the history of the Sun's system."

Alpha Centauri, Our Home System Where Conditions for Life like Ours Are More Ideal than They Are within the Sun's System.

"I am about to move into interstellar space to complete a mission to the constellation of Lyra," Akon said. "I am going there to observe a supernova. We are now replenishing my spaceship from the vast mothership, and we will have some time together for you to understand the history of this system in which you live, my dear."

"Oh!" I said, and stopped. I could say no more. I suddenly felt the moment charged with that particular poignancy and deep emotion that always threatens my self-control.

With a lump in my throat, I watched Akon's dear face, as he gently said, "Calm your questing mind and relax in the happiness of the present. Whatever may happen in time, there is always a reason for it."

"How can I live through time with the trackless fathoms of space separating us like the darkness of eternal night?"

"Beloved one, I shall be with you always," Akon softly replied. "Our destiny is bound together. A telepathic link binds our souls in eternal love. Our lives are entwined as a thread of gold weaves a pattern in the sky."

Gently he put his hand under my chin, tilting my head up and back, and looked deep into my eyes.

"My love, my life, my chosen mate," he whispered, his voice soft with emotion. "I will return to possess you, and sow the seed of my love within your delicate body. The mark of my love will remain within your soul forever."

Gathering me up in his arms, he held me close for a moment before carrying me out of the luxurious room and away along a wide and beautiful stairway.

Silently we passed over the rich, thick carpeting and down a spacious passageway. I glanced into the airy rooms we passed, bright with glorious colors, where many people relaxed. Other people moved about us—men, women and children. They smiled their greetings as they went about their various duties within the great spaceship. All were fair of complexion, tall and beautiful, soft-spoken and gentle and moving with a natural grace and rhythm.

The women wore simple and diaphanous apparel, low-cut and gathered around the waist to fall in graceful folds to the ankles. These garments were of classic beauty in different exotic colors. They shimmered with a silky sheen, folding over the contours of the naked bodies underneath and caressing the skin with a silky touch. All the women had bare and lovely feet, and they moved with the ease and freedom of perfect health.

The men wore very simple silk garments, a form of close-fitting knee breeches, with no covering to hide the natural strength and beauty of their feet, while the children wore the same type of silk garment—just a single garment with nothing underneath.

"I'm glad I left my shoes under the divan," I said. "I feel so out of place in these heavy clothes. I wish I could wear one of those lovely silk garments that allow one's body to breathe. They look so very relaxing. There is no extreme of climate unless you step out onto the surface of an alien planet. That is why you were wearing the type of uniform you are. You even covered your feet, because you stepped out of your spaceship when you landed for me."

"Harmony of movement in time with your mind this first time has been very successful," Akon laughed as he swiftly set me on my feet again in a beautiful room. "I focused your mind on moving with the spaceship and not on extraneous things such as clothes."

"How lovely it is here!" I exclaimed. "Not only the beauty and comfort of our surroundings, but also the perfect beauty of communication and words. Humans of the Sun's system have lost the art of words and communication. Not for them the beauty of writing and words. They can now only express themselves in short, sharp syllables like the grunting of so many primitives. They have lost the art of their mother tongue through laziness and the continuous watching of television, and by never taking part in anything themselves."

"It depends on the programs presented, my beloved. Now, look."

There was color everywhere! Rose red predominated in the carpeting and wall coverings. The low, comfortable seats were made of a soft golden material with threads of emerald green and violet like the colors of the spectrum. A tall man with his arms folded across his chest stood watching a scene in the electric mirage that shimmered in minute detail across the far end of the room.

Turning, he came toward us and placed both his hands on my shoulders, and kissed me on both cheeks.

"I'm happy Akon has found you," the man said. "Welcome, my dear, to our civilization. Akon's work as a scientist is sometimes dangerous, though. You must have courage. Never forget this."

I looked into his golden eyes, so kindly and concerned. As he returned my long look, I understood how unknown the future would be.

"I am tuned in to the vibration of our home planet in the star system of Alpha Centauri," he continued in his quiet, gentle voice, "our home system where conditions for life like ours are more ideal than they are within the Sun's system. The broader ecosphere—the area surrounding a star where conditions permit development and the existence of life as we know it—is intensified by a binary system. This support of life and advanced development on the planets revolving in orbit about our stars is caused by the radiations and ultraviolet emanations that produce their oxygen atmosphere. Our home planet is well within this stupendous radiating ecosphere, which is further augmented by a third star similar to the Sun. Thus the vibratory rate is higher and ideal for the advanced development of our civilization. The home system is a triplex system, receiving the radiations from three stars similar to the Sun but four light-years away, or 38 billion kilometers. It would take an astronaut from Earth four years to reach Alpha Centauri—that is, if he were able to travel with the speed of light as Earth scientists understand it. With our spaceships, this distance is instantly annihilated.

"Our civilization existed on Earth eons ago, after we moved out from the mother planet, Venus. We were advised by our scientists to do so at that time in the history of the Sun's system, as the Sun was breathing out its breath of life in the cosmic cycle of solar expansion. The Sun has, in the past, shown signs of its variable nature, the corona expanding out with lethal radiations to engulf the planets, destroying all flora and fauna. This occurs in cycles of time. It is a natural phenomenon, and stars of this nature are observed very closely by us."

"Then your civilization originated in this solar system," I exclaimed with joy. "How wonderful! There is a link between us. People on Earth are not alien."

"Indeed, that is so. Our great civilization flourished for thousands of years on Earth, before we moved out to a neighboring solar system where the stars are stable suns suitable for our way of life. We left some of our people on Earth and on Mars, but through the centuries the environment of the variable star, the Sun, has had a negative effect on their thinking and way of life. They became thoughtless and destructive, nearly wrecking Earth many times, and turning Mars into a desert.

"Venus died in the last cycle of solar expansion when all flora and fauna were destroyed by lethal stellar radiations. Her proximity to the star of her system caused our scientists to study the Sun very closely. They found that the Sun's atmosphere engulfs the planetary system, and that any changes occurring in the Sun would affect the planets and their atmospheres.

"The star of this system is a middle-aged, yellow variable, somewhat irregular in the radiation of short wavelengths. We all live within the ecosphere of our stars, and the stability of each planet within a solar system depends on the radiations emitted by the stars.

"The Sun has a tendency toward instability within the gaseous envelope. As the rotational velocity is slowing down, magnetic flip-flops occur in a cycle that varies between seven and seventeen years, averaging about eleven years. Magnetic polarity is reversed at each cycle, and sunspots are triggered by magnetism, emitting brilliant and lethal solar flares. These flares erupt through the photosphere to spew out ionized hydrogen— streams of fast protons and electrons—toward the planets in the form of deadly solar winds.

"The electron density in the Earth's ionosphere waxes and wanes in step with the eleven-year cycle. Likewise, the auroral displays aloft wax and wane as planet Earth respires within her star's atmosphere.

"The Earth's ozone layer can be destroyed during a cycle of the Sun's expansion, as the ozone layer of Venus was destroyed, exposing the surface to radiation and thereby destroying all vegetation. Earth survived the last cycle of solar expansion, though it killed off vast numbers of terrible lizards that had flourished extravagantly in the subtropical climate. For millions of years these dinosaurs had dominated Earth, their thick hides like armor plates, a protection against radiation bombardment during that epoch of explosive evolution when the Sun was younger and the climate of Earth very much warmer.

"Thriving on violence and destruction, their small, weak brains filtered such dim impressions as their limited senses received. They were no match for their changing environment, and when the Sun burst forth in expansive eruption, engulfing your solar system in lethal radiations, they were destroyed over the entire land surface of the planet and in the swamps and shallow seas.

"The Earth, reacting like a barometer to her star, reversed poles in cataclysmic eruptions all over her surface, burying this thriving life within her breast. While her star shrinks back, smaller and brighter, as each cycle of expansion takes its toll in her scale of evolution, the period of time between each regular period of sweeping death shortens. The aging star is moving again in this epoch to a death throe of expansive radiations.

"Earth lies well within the great radiating atmosphere of the Sun. The tenuous corona extends so far from the visible disk that Mercury, Venus, Earth and its Moon and Mars are enveloped in it. Undoubtedly, these intensified radiations now emitted from the Sun will disturb the Earth's ionosphere, increasing ionization of the outer atmosphere. This in turn will trigger unstable weather patterns throughout the world, affecting global air circulation and rainfall patterns. During the cycle of low-density sunspot activity, droughts occur, and during the cycle of high-density sunspot activity, severe storms and floods occur. The Sun affects the weather all the time as the wind patterns change, and this in turn affects the surface of the planet, causing numerous earthquakes. When the planets of the solar system move into conjunction, they will exert a pull on Earth and many severe earthquakes will occur. The prospects for humankind are chilling. They live in an interglacial period and are now moving into another cycle of vast weather changes, which is a prelude to another ice age.

"The physics of planet Earth cannot be studied without reference first to her star, the Sun."

I Lived Again in the Magic of the Vision I Had Had while Lying Alone in Hospital when I Was Given the Magic Lease We Sense as Life.

The tall scientist switched on the electric mirage and went on to say his name was Theton. He was working in close cooperation with Akon in the scientific surveillance of this solar system.

"Look at the Sun in the electric mirage," I whispered, my voice refusing to sound as I watched the enormous writhing sphere. It erupted into vast prominences that suddenly collapsed, only to rise again immediately like live things—some awful creatures of the space depths—violently agitated by turbulent motion with ascending and descending currents. A granulated appearance made up of millions of cells resembling those of a honeycomb pulsated in a boiling ferment of electrical disturbance. Jets of glowing hydrogen erupted, reaching out with immense tentacles to engulf us.

"How violent and frightening it is! Is your scientific survey ship really immune to those magnetic upheavals near the photosphere?" I asked as a flash of apprehension filled my mind and I moved closer to Akon.

"Be happy now. Our love is a being, a timeless flame. It is the bond of our souls, and the soul is a flame that never dies. My beloved, you know of this, so do not continue to fret."

Looking down at me with a gentle smile of rebuke, he brushed the hair from my cheek and kissed me.

"We never think of such things," said Haben, quietly interjecting his thoughtful concern. "Akon's spaceship is highly efficient, with our latest technical achievements."

I felt little comfort from his reassuring words, however, as I watched the boiling, expanding gases of the convection region with widening eyes and a catch in my breath. They writhed brilliantly in continuous waves, and branches of light emitted outward from the photosphere in dense radiations. Stupendous energy and density are generated continuously, and radiation is the process of transfer deep inside the Sun—the photo-electric process of bluish radiations.

Suddenly, a gigantic vortex in the Sun's equatorial region commenced to rotate and darken with the intensity of its magnetic field. The awesome, terrifying solar storm—or sunspot—erupted and spewed out a gale of ionized particles in a fantastic flare that engulfed the spaceship.

"I set the automatic control in my ship to release a laboratory disk to collect a sample of that flare plasma," Akon remarked.

"Good," Theton replied. "I think analysis of that flare type is urgent."

"Akon is our scientist in charge of variable star research," Haben told me.

"Have you ever been really close to a star?" I asked.

My heart turned over as Akon smiled and said, "Not as close as I wish to go for scientific observation. It is now necessary to make a closer approach to study the photosphere. We must take samples of the boiling gas in order to counteract the dangerous reactions within the magnetic vortices, or sunspots, before the next maximum cycle."

"Oh . . ." I said, and again, a sudden apprehension clouded my happiness. What fate awaited me? I wondered why I felt such a deep feeling of unease as I watched with awe the frightful violence of the Sun.

I looked with concern at Haben. Meeting my eyes, he knew my thoughts and fears for Akon's safety. I looked back at the filtered mirage into the Sun's inferno. The violent upheavals of our star held the portents of dire and terrible disaster unless Akon could approach close enough to nullify the explosion conditions. Although the star's existence was a source of life-giving light for the entire system, I sensed its dangerous hostility to any form of control. As a live thing, it would react.

Akon stood, watching carefully every phase of the Sun's violent activity. His tall, lithe figure seemed to become greater and more powerful, his wonderful face more godlike with the intensity of his concentration. I thought of the teeming life on Earth and knew how little they could understand the mighty and powerful forces set in motion to stabilize their star and wobbling planet. How could they know that Akon held the key to life and their continued existence? Clearly, I could now see and understand the divine writing on the blackboard of space. Here was the reality for me.

Slowly, the fantastic close-up scene of the Sun faded away until nothing was left but the length of the sumptuous room.

"We must return to my spaceship now," Akon softly said.

"That means . . . " My voice faltered, and I could say no more.

Akon put his arm round my shoulders and held me close while a tall and lovely woman glided silently into the room, her bare feet sinking without a sound into the thick and rich carpeting.

She came to me and kissed me on both cheeks and wished me farewell, her golden eyes soft and thoughtful, her beautiful face full of concern.

"I know how you feel," she said. "I am Pleia, Haben's mate. When we mate, it is forever, and so it will be for you and Akon. He will be back for you before long."

Pushing her shining blonde hair back over her shoulders, she took Theton's hand.

"Theton is my brother. When we bring the giant mothership into Earth's atmosphere, you will know that Akon is safely back."

"Come," called Haben. "We will go back to the garden room on the way, where I will show you our home planet as I promised."

"Thank you," I replied. "How wonderful that will be."

Smiling gently, Haben motioned us to follow him and we all went back into the garden room and sat down in the luxurious comfort of a deep, low couch, while he attached the tiny roll to a groove in the wall. A distant planet appeared, a bright pinpoint of light rapidly enlarging—another home of life, another island moving in the vast void of heaven.

Here Was the Reality, a Dimension I Could Only Perceive after Releasing My Tie with Earth.

With beating heart, I saw a brilliant blue-white sphere coming closer and closer as if we were flying there ourselves. Then Akon was speaking.

"Our home system in Alpha Centauri consists of seven planets, all inhabited by our civilization. The seven planets orbit about the third component of this beautiful star system, known to you as Proxima Centauri. The largest star gives a reddish light about one-third as bright as the Sun's, while the second star's light is similar to sunlight. The third star, Proxima Centauri, is like the Sun, only with a reddish light. And, of course, it is a very stable star. The planet we see now is our original home planet in this triplex system, similar to Venus when she was able to harbor our great civilization in the past. Since we moved to this planet, we have expanded out to all the other planets in the system. The entire system is within the tremendous coronas of the three stars."

Through breaks in the clouds, the beautifully colored surface of the planet appeared, and we seemed to hover high in the atmosphere. A great, glistening cloud billowed up over the sea with a curtain of rain at its base. It was a magnificent cumulus, clear and graceful. The immense double circle of a brilliantly colored rainbow floated within its aqueous influence—a rainbow seen as a complete circle from high in the sky, its colors bright and clear with a depth of beauty only possible in the rain-washed atmosphere. Rose red shimmered in the outer primary circle, quite breathtaking in its entirety. The rays from the stars struck a golden radiance out of the cloud, and the whole sky reflected a covenant of color with the celestial consciousness of the universe.

The divine essence of truth encompassed my being, and there was no sadness or emotion in knowing the transient joy of being a part of this life. I knew it could not last forever. Now was the time to live, though, to tune in to the essence of life and to become a part of it so that I could live with it for the rest of my life, no matter where.

A vast expanse of dark blue sea spread out below and small land masses, lighter in color, appeared scattered over the darkness of the water. A deep blue sky reflected in the depths of the seas. The expanse of mighty ocean curved beyond the hazy horizon, tranquil and calm, sparkling in the soft, clear light from the stars.

Moving in closer, we saw a great island spread out below, emerald hills and mountain slopes rising in the misty distance to mountaintops of rose-red rocks and cliffs glowing in the gentle radiance of sunlight. Throughout the pastoral country, tall dark-green trees could be seen scattered in park-like beauty, with winding rivers and streams glittering from the mountains to the sea. Enormous golden trees like deodars stood out on the mountain slopes, where sapphire blue and emerald green met in a glory of sunlit atmosphere. The island scene of my vision, and even the fragrance of the lovely countryside, filled my senses as memory flooded my being. I lived again in the magic of the vision I had had while lying alone in hospital, when I was given the magic lease we sense as life, that messenger of joy. I felt the inner lifting of the spirit toward the vaster firmament beyond, where time is of our mortal essence. Here was the reality, a dimension I could only perceive after releasing my tie with Earth.

"Our Dimension Is Space and the Surface of Planets— Never the Interior of Planets."

We moved with the electric mirage as if we were hovering over the glorious countryside ourselves, with fantastic and complete mobility and unlimited vision.

"This scene is coming through from one of our small surveillance disks, transmitting directly to us," Akon explained. "There is no time lag. The scene is instantly beamed to us, as the disk is robot controlled."

The disk moved to a lower altitude, and I saw white animals racing across the emerald sward below—horses, pure white with flying manes and tails, galloping over the open countryside. Others quietly grazed as foals frolicked among them. There were no fences to hem them in and no roads or highways to gash and mutilate the glorious land. No pylons, hideous constructions or railway tracks marched across the fair land like monsters of the airy depths.

Here was no civilization of the machine age but an Earth untouched by any artificial means of cultivation or transportation. Here was freedom and joy amidst a land of plenty—the tranquil pastoral beauty of a lovely land. Scattered homes could be seen nestling amongst the trees and flowers, circular buildings made of a glistening material like mother-of-pearl set on daises of surrounding circular steps.

Rising in our slow passage over the glorious country, we approached the high mountains and glided over the mighty rose-red cliffs, slowly descending to the rolling green hills beyond, and on to the sea. Silver craft moved about the sky, their round fuselages glinting in the sunlit atmosphere like the iridescent lining of a pearl shell, flashing signals of welcome to our observation disk and other signals direct to the giant spaceship hovering in the environment of the Sun's system.

A city sparkled, white and silver, encircling a curve of bay. The deep sapphire water reflected a wealth of classic beauty set among trees and flowers full of brilliant and exotic colors. There were simple, circular buildings, not more than two or three stories high, with flat tops where individual craft could land, take off or park. Some of the buildings were enormous, like great circular pyramids with vast columns and steps encircling the bases, but with no roads or highways to mar the beauty of the scene.

Completely lost in the fantastic beauty of the place with its wide lawns and lovely trees, gleaming buildings and exotic colors, I heard Akon speak again.

"We have no problems with smog or atmospheric pollution, as we use only electricity generated from the atmosphere for all our energy and power needs. The various individual sky ships used by everybody are electrical—they simply tap the energy from the atmosphere."

Suddenly, the magnificent picture faded away and nothing was left but the length of the sumptuous room again. Each time this happened, I felt quite disorientated, so I quietly remained seated.

Without a word, Akon took my hand and we went out of the giant spaceship and stepped again into the central cabin of his scientific survey ship. A gentle humming and sense of quiet vibration through the floor gave me a feeling of security as it had done when first I stepped into this beautiful spaceship. In the larger vessel I had not heard or felt any movement at all.

A moment later, the second member of the crew came through from the mothership. He was tall and very handsome, but younger than Akon. He smiled, a fascinating expression lighting up his face and bringing warmth to his eyes. His brilliant white teeth flashed with fleeting charm, and chestnut hair and golden eyes accentuated his striking appearance. Here indeed was a man to shoulder responsibilities with Akon.

As he went to the control panel, the flickering screen lit his face, sharpening the fine molding of his features. "My name is Sheron," he said in a deep, gentle voice. "My ancestors remained on Earth to study the Pleistocene cycle of solar expansion. They constructed a beautiful underground city where they survived the intense radiations. Moving into the heart of the great mountains of the southern continent, they maintained our civilization there. Even to this epoch on Earth, our spaceships come and go, retaining this base within the vast wastes of Antarctica.'"

"And the North Pole in the Arctic?" I asked.

"Our civilization set up headquarters in the Southern Hemisphere only, as this was merely a prelude to our departure for a neighboring star system. The radiations in the Sun's system had become far too intense for our well-being and we were forced to live underground. This, of course, was not to our liking, so we moved out of this solar system altogether, to the surface of another planet where we can still enjoy the glory of the skies, the stars, the fresh winds with the tang of the sea and the rain, and the infinite reaches of the heavens."

"Do you wear the type of garment that Akon was wearing when he stepped from this ship on the mountaintop to protect your skin against radiation from the Sun?"

"Yes, indeed, my dear. We never expose our skin to radiation from the Sun. As a scientist, I am continuing with the work of my parents and our ancestors, in the study and research into variable stars—still a dangerous mission for both Akon and me. We look into the very beginnings of life throughout our galaxy, for we are all evolved from stardust. We are star people, and thus a part of the living galaxy in which we sense this magic lease we know as life. You, my dear, are aware of this because you are one of us. In time, we will all be together again, forever, in the cycle of our destiny, which is entwined in eternity."

"Our people have never been troglodytes," Akon quietly said. "Our dimension is space and the surface of planets—never the interior of planets. Underground cities and passages are a legacy of the past, left to Earth by us. We retain the underground base at the South Pole, where the warm lakes are. This is the area of the underground city of our ancestors and in that epoch there was no ice cap. Volcanic activity keeps the area of lakes free of ice and snow, and we are able to move out of the spaceships in comfort due to the lack of radiation at that high latitude. There is a hole in the atmosphere there, through which the circumpolar vortex spirals down with the intensity of the Earth's magnetic field over the poles.

"At the poles, the Earth's magnetic fields dip earthward in a funnel-shaped pattern. As solar particles spiral down toward Earth in the magnetic funnels above the poles, they hit and excite atoms in the upper air that give off the flashing spectral light of the auroras. These streams of charged particles from the Sun wax and wane with the eleven-year solar cycle as flares burst from the surface and bombard the Earth with radiation channelled toward the poles along the lines of force of the Earth's magnetic field. These particles are trapped and swept from pole to pole, and they are moving fast enough—and in sufficient numbers—to excite the molecules of the ionosphere to emit their characteristic luminous spectra. The areas on the Earth's surface from which auroral displays aloft are observed wax and wane with the eleven-year cycle of solar activity. In its output of light in the far ultraviolet range of the spectrum, unobservable at the Earth's surface, the Sun is a variable star.

"The electrified curtain of the auroras cuts right across the Antarctic continent, as the southern auroral zone is centered about the south magnetic pole, which is over a thousand kilometers from the geographical south pole. The south pole itself is on a high, windless plateau, where powder snow lies unbroken above hundreds of meters of compacted ice. Antarctica is the coldest and windiest region. It is much colder than the Arctic, where the relatively thin ice over the Arctic Ocean allows warming of the atmosphere from below, while the air above Antarctica has no such central heating system. It lies over a massive continent, and it is literally in an ice age. Temperatures of 100 degrees below freezing can result. As a result, the insulating roof of the troposphere disappears in midwinter, leaving the lower atmosphere open to outer space."

Sheron pressed buttons on the control panel to disengage the spaceship as Akon finished speaking, and we sat down on the comfortable bench. The door closed silently and merged with the shining curved wall. The viewing lens flickered on to show the giant mothership floating in the velvet blackness of space, the radiation from the Sun striking its enormous shape with a stark white light against the background of brilliant stars. Beyond it I saw Earth—so alone and vulnerable, a delicate shade of blue with cloud patterns swirling white—a home of life, an island moving in the vast void of heaven.

I thought of my family so far away on that remote sphere, that ball floating in the trackless reaches of space. I drew in my breath at the incredible scene and felt the remoteness and restlessness that only a mother can experience. Akon drew me close to him and pressed a button at the base of the lens with his foot. The lens darkened and went blank. He began to speak again, in his gentle, reassuring voice.

"As I mentioned before, the Sun's corona extends so far from the visible disk that the Earth is enveloped in it, so you can understand how the weather on Earth is controlled by the Sun. Magnetic storms in the ionosphere are worldwide since the ring current encircles the Earth and the global circulation of the atmosphere is powered by the Sun."

"So then is your base situated at the magnetic pole?" I asked with renewed interest.

"We are at the center of the Antarctic auroral zone, the southern terminus of the three key meridians." Akon quoted so many degrees west, east and east, then went on. "This is the region where magnetic instruments go haywire and the compass needle dips down at the magnetic pole. Radio communication cutoffs occur, and disturbance is so severe during the cycles of maximum activity on the Sun that sudden radio fadeouts occur simultaneously with the appearance of solar flares. At these high latitudes, the deviation of the compass needle and radio fadeouts occur also during the cycle of minimum solar activity. The dislocation of ordinary compass navigation is common within the auroral zone."

"Is your base near any of the observation stations maintained by Earth nations?" I asked.

"Yes, indeed. The French have a forward station in the immediate area of the south magnetic pole, some three hundred kilometers toward the geographic pole from their main station on the coast, while the Russians are also our neighbors with two observation stations in the area of the magnetic pole. The Americans have their pole station at the geographical south pole, where ionospheric observations are made through long periods of total darkness when there is no direct radiation from the Sun to ionize it and also for mapping worldwide magnetic storms at a key point on the Earth's surface.

"We regard these endeavors by Earth scientists very highly," Akon continued. "In the hostile environment of the polar regions, they have conducted themselves with great determination and courage. South African scientists have discovered a death trap above Cape Town and the South Atlantic, where there is a tendency toward the formation of a third-world magnetic pole that bends radiation downward. This danger-ous radiation now penetrates deep into the atmosphere, and the anomaly, an area of magnetic disturbances can be the prelude to a polar region of intense magnetic power."

"Is this an example of polar wandering?" I asked, deeply interested.

"The direction in which the axis of the main dipole field of the Earth lies has changed markedly over the eons of geological time, quite apart from the changes in the polarity of the dipole. The north pole has wan-dered from a point in America, over the Pacific, and up through Siberia to its present position, and so on. Stars and planets are forever changing— nothing in the galaxy is static.

"We found the pyramidal type of construction most suitable for Earth and Mars, where many earthquakes plagued us and radiation remained a hazard. The pyramids were constructed by us and used by later civiliza-tions as places of worship and for burial. They are cosmic libraries, and in time they will point the way to the stars. The human race of Earth will find an escape route to the stars and away from the violence within the Sun's system that its variable nature creates. These pointers will give them the clues. Those who find these clues will be eligible and free to fol-low us into the fathomless depths of space beyond the light barrier.

"The Moon is alien to this star system. It came with Jupiter and its retinue of planets. Jupiter is a forming star—a star condensing—and thus it retains a high velocity of rotation, a large mass, low density and the usual heat in the core retained by the star. It is a solar system within a solar system. Seven of Jupiter's planets have retained atmospheres and life as we know it. The Moon's scarred and pitted face was the direct result of her star's explosion. It was cremated beyond recognition of its former splendor. It is dead and lifeless, like other asteroids and planets in eternal orbit around waxing stars and planets, or like those forming a vast orbit of their own where they gather as flotsam in a cemetery of the solar system.

"The Earth and its companion formed a binary system as it is to this time. Through magnetic distortion, vast changes occurred on Earth at the time of conjunction, and all life has been of a predacious nature.

"Stars wax and wane. They live on as planets, creating and harboring life on their surface. Planets also die and become asteroids, meteorites and wanderers in space for all eternity. Quasars are an early stage in the life of galaxies, which also wax and wane, held in orbit by the magnetic field of a metagalaxy. Millions of galaxies speed in orbit about this super-system, which we can now detect with our instruments.

"All galaxies have a force dependence on a larger structure that remains inaccessible to observation. This state exists throughout the intergalactic medium, and is common to all galaxies, ad infinitum. Galaxies have their life cycles. They attain globular clusters, gathered up by the magnetic fields of mature galaxies like the Milky Way. Revolving in close orbit around the spiral star system, remaining in the surrounding halo of the galaxy, and then drawn between the spiral arms as magnetic fields intensify, they remain in eternal matter as the mighty vortex storm of the galaxy condenses and finds another haven in yet another waxing galaxy or island universe.

"As stars sweep up interstellar gas, so galaxies sweep up intergalactic gas in the halo shock front, where star formation occurs. As the age of the galaxy increases, accretion is checked by the expulsion of hydrogen from the nucleus and a lessening of magnetic fields. Spatial imbalance occurs in clusters of galaxies, causing the nucleus of a star system to blow up violently due to unstable conditions before it can escape into the general field.

"Clusters of galaxies are formed from condensing intergalactic gas clouds spinning about their minor axes. Gravity then rules the rotation of galaxies, and they form and have their existence and move in fields of matter and anti-matter, and we have our existence within them. We live in our own part of space-time, within the limits of our galaxy, like a rainbow, peculiar to each observer's position. Yet we are intercommunicable. Our private rainbow systems are different, for you and I can see to a certain distance into space from a different point. The forces affecting me in function of the universe, must affect you through me," Akon quietly concluded.

*Akon's craft as photographed by
the author.*

"As you now understand, my dear," Sheron gently said, "Akon communicated with you many years ago from the other side of the rainbow, and you knew he was there, out there, in another extension of space-time, living in another solar system within the same galaxy. Earth time is only what you make it because of the speed of Earth in orbit around the Sun, the Earth's rotation and the speed of the entire system around the vast disk of the galaxy, according to the system's position in the galaxy. And relative to our position in the galaxy, our home system gives us another dimension in space-time.

"By altering the wavelength of our ships moving in a vacuum, we are able to come into the Earth's space-time and materialize in Earth's skies. Now you know what it is like beyond the rainbow—away beyond the light barrier and out of this solar system where, in times to come, we will take you with us.

"Is it really possible to take me with you?" I asked with a catch of wonder in my breath.

"Of course," Akon replied. "This is why we are conditioning you to it now."

"The beauty and violence of our galactic system harbors millions of other star systems similar to the Sun's system," Akon explained, "where the cosmic rays emanating from the vast nucleus create life throughout, as in countless other galaxies. There is continuous creation of energy and matter from the cloud of hydrogen gas in the nucleus as it spreads out in the galactic vortex, condensing into matter, with the cosmic rays touching off the existence of life from the divine reservoir of short-length energy. Creation is infinite. Continuous creation and evolution gives to the mind of humankind the speed of time. Time is the process of thinking into the fourth dimension, added to the three dimensions of matter, or planetary surfaces, matched by the perpetual motion of the inner consciousness to the perpetual motion of the galaxy in different time speeds to each and every solar system.

"Venus, the cradle of humankind, remained shrouded and bereft of life after the Pleistocene cycle of solar expansion, its fruitful eons of fertility at an end and its vast warm seas that nurtured our beginning dried out and barren. But her glory still remains as a reality in the electric mirage, perfected by her progeny, who were compelled to move from her protective surface out into the far reaches of space to propagate their species on the surface of an alien planet called Earth. There we adapted to the different time-speed on a younger planet.

"Laying claim to Earth as a host to life, we continued to perfect our spaceships in readiness for the time when we would have to leave this solar system, prior to another wave of mass extinctions from the system's star. We knew we would have to adapt to an entirely new dimension of time as we prepared our spaceships to move into the fathomless reaches of interstellar space, and on reaching the constellation of Centaurus, we would need to adapt ourselves to a higher vibratory rate of light and time on the surface of our chosen planet.

"Now, as the old dimension passes away into the nebulous mists of time, we can only look back into the electric mirage, which retains our past for us, to see the glory of our civilization in the time of the Venus period. Now we have moved beyond that time barrier in the solar system into the time of a highly advanced system, stable and beautiful, without the violence of variable stars.

"You, my dear, have adapted well to our time dimension. We are not creatures apart in the material body. The reality lies in our magnetic link with our parent stars. Each solar system throughout the living galaxy is relative. All living creatures on the planets are connected—their brains emit radio waves and their hearts electrical rhythms in unison with the star of their system.

"Until people of Earth discover this truth, they will continue to destroy themselves and all around them." Akon's stern warning cut across my consciousness like a knife.

"There is a strange urgency to the question of their space flight propulsion," he continued. "It is a fact that their star, the Sun, is dying, or changing in the cycles of time. It is purely a metamorphosis. They need to pool all their scientific knowledge and ability to perfect space travel and seek another waxing star. They must stop their eternal warring among themselves before it is too late and the Sun expands again in its cycle of lethal radiation.

"The vast amount of human energy and time now being spent on rocket research is of no avail. It will not solve the problem of interstellar travel. Men of Earth continue to fight with violence to attain power over others while their planet is in mortal danger, and the selfishness of nations restrains a struggling humanity from becoming aware of the portents of danger encircling their world."

"Is there a possibility of helping them to accelerate their space program?" I asked. "The fantastic light propulsion of your spaceships—can you not explain to them your alien science?"

The lines down Akon's cheeks etched deeper with the sternness of his reply.

"The stage of evolution reached by humankind on Earth forbids any form of communication or support. Only when they change their attitude of mind—when they become gentle and peace-loving and have the ability to love and cherish all fauna and flora on their planet—will we contact them. At the present time, they have still not acquired spiritual advancement. They crawl and live upon the bottom of their atmospheric seas like slugs of the airy depths attuned to their immediate environment. Their eyes are sensitive to only a limited segment of the spectrum of light, and their senses are dulled by their material existence.

"Gone is the enlightenment of yore, the individual perception. Gone is the ideal life of the great universal civilization, moving in rhythm with the universe in cycles visible and invisible, which removed all uncertainty from life and provided the cosmic certainty on which civilizations thrive. In this present cycle of Earth time, we find our universal human civilization collapsed, with only fragments of its secrets surviving in isolated civilizations of antiquity. This poor restless planet now harbors a race of humans confused and overcome by the forces of evil. This was created by their own low spiritual energy, and they resort to aggressive violence and destruction of their own species in frantic attempts to recapture the old magic.

"Some withdraw before the growing confusion, dedicating themselves and their successors to preserving a spiritual tradition and participating in the dreamlike current of life where all men experience a state of union with the universe—or to them, God.

"The whole process of degeneration on Earth has been accompanied by a flood of words from social and political reformers, religious leaders and philosophers. Vast stacks of books lie dormant in libraries through-out the world, their meaning misunderstood and lost in a torrent of many words. Words written or spoken cannot solve the problems of Earth, as it becomes ever more apparent that fresh combinations of words fail to penetrate the barrier of thought and prejudice among humans on Earth. The whole level of human consciousness must be raised to enable us to cooperate in any field of philosophy or science.

"We can only observe and contain them on their planet, while the conditioned attitudes of the human hordes cease to hold opinions as freshly inspired tyrants drive them on and over the bodies of their pre-decessors. This action solves the problem of such civilizations, which cannot attain enlightenment and harmony, but must destroy themselves within the violence to which they have been conditioned. We live in a violent universe. Unless men of Earth can learn to detach themselves and escape from the forces of violence in which their existence is set, they are doomed to eternal destruction.

"Men of Earth are misusing the holy secrets of nature, even causing magnetic lines of force to be irretrievably disrupted." Akon went on, again condemning the stupidity of humankind on Earth. "It is indeed sad to observe the way they are poisoning the priceless gift of their glorious atmosphere. Stupidity and ignorance are the causes of this devastation. The flora and fauna are now suffering in the murky depths created by the mindless folly of humankind. In times to come, they will smother in their own filth like bloated slugs groping in the smog of disaster.

"We can remain only for very short periods of time in the Sun's sys-tem. To land on Earth and remain in her atmosphere for any length of time is becoming increasingly impossible because of the amount of pollu-tion that now exists. Only in the high foothills of the mountains can we now breathe with comfort the life-giving air of Earth."

"Is it not possible even now to show people of Earth the way to spiritual and scientific survival?" I persisted. "The way your civilization achieved it?"

"Indeed, we can show them. But the differences are apparently insur-mountable. Earth's authorities have shown an aggressive reaction to our approach, giving orders to their air forces to shoot us down, or as that is impossible, to ram our spaceships with their own craft to bring our ships to ground. In this way, they could hope to find access to our superior technology, which of course is all they want. Under these circumstances, we do not contact heads of governments or military authorities.

"The responsibilities of administration and organization lie with us—the scientists. We make decisions and control all aspects of life within our civilization. The key to our science retains our control and freedom throughout the galaxy, as we tap and use this cosmic energy and generate electricity from the atmospheres of planets for our power needs. Our propulsion system for spaceships is the only true escape route to the stars, and we guard these secrets of our science with our lives against misuse by other civilizations."

CHAPTER 5

THE HEIGHTS OF CATHKIN

A thing of beauty, Earth moves there, floating in the fathomless depths of space. The planet is alone and unprotected, vulnerable, yet nourishing the form of humankind, an atom of beauty and life floating there against the unwinking stars, who are indifferent to her fate. She is a minute atom in the vast circumference of the galaxy, yet she harbors the specter of man the predator.

Looming closer in the lens, Earth's higher atmosphere glowed to form a hazy pink crescent around the shadow side—Earth's shadow, a dark azure blue between the glow and the surface. The rounded body of the planet lay still in darkness as the gold and blue of sunrise streaked the atmospheric bands with translucent veils, the dark curve of the planet concealing the flaring disk of the Sun as it rotated smoothly beneath us.

I saw the deep violet-blue of the high atmosphere, and then we came in through the counterglow to land with a featherlike touchdown on the top of the hill. Akon looked deep into my eyes with tender concern, willing me to accept without question the moment of parting.

"We now return you to the hill on which I found you, my beloved," he whispered, drawing me close. "I shall return soon."

We moved toward the curved wall of the spaceship and the door slid back into the double walls. We stepped out onto the hull and back to the soil of Earth as the Sun set over the Drakensberg in the west.

Sheron waved from the open doorway with a flashing smile. With a lump in my throat, I turned to Akon. Gently, he kissed me, and without a word we both turned away.

Quickly I walked away from the great ship as the door closed behind Akon's tall figure. I moved out of range as the ship rose straight up to hover for a moment high in the sky, catching the last rays of the Sun, which flashed in rainbow colors around it. For a moment it seemed to merge into the counterglow before moving with a sudden burst of light into the rising shadow of Earth. And then they were gone, in a flash of brilliant light, back into the fathomless seas of space and away beyond the light barrier, where the uncharted void of timelessness rules the destiny of planets.

It was rapidly getting dark as I turned homeward. The homestead lay some three miles away, nestled in a valley in the rolling grass country of the Drakensberg foothills. The mountains were dark now against the glow in the west, except for the winding ribbon of track over the pass.

As I stood alone in the veld, there was a sudden rustling. *Abafana* broke cover out of the long grass, scattering like a covey of quail, the whites of their eyes showing with fright in the gloom. I called to them in Zulu, telling them not to be afraid of the great wagon in the sky, but my words fell on deaf ears. No explanation could still the overpowering, superstitious fear of anything so fantastic in the sky, and the children ran on in silent fright back to their *kya*[1] in the valley.

Old Muti, the *induna* and cook, would be the first to hear the tale. It would be told with extravagant embellishment by the eldest *umfana*, who would run like a hare through the grass back to the farmhouse kitchen. Muti had taken over the family affairs, stepping into Ladam's place after the old man died. The high altitude and cold winters had shortened Ladam's lifespan, and I missed the watchful glance of his wise old eyes and the wisdom of his gentle philosophy.

Nobody had questioned the decision made by Muti to take Ladam's place, and he wielded his authority with clever and wily foresight, summing up the nature of the *umlungu*[2] with a façade of respectable honesty. I could not remain silent, I thought. I needed to tell my sister the whole

---

1. *home*
2. *white man*

story before she heard it from Muti. As I saw the soft glow of lamplight from the farmhouse windows, I blessed the dim light of lamps and candles, which would afford a gentle cover for the radiance in my eyes. But my sister would know the moment she saw my face anyway—there could be no secrets in this house.

I Was Brought Back to the Realization of Earth Time by the Zulu Maid Bringing the Early Morning Tea.

The next morning I awoke from a deep and refreshing sleep and stretched my limbs in an ecstasy of happiness. Glancing through the wide open window, I noticed the Sun glinting on the tops of the gum trees—that same fearful Sun, a glaring, intense sphere of lethal radiation floating in the void of space. I could never forget how the great writhing disk had engulfed us with its immensity through the viewing lens in the spaceship. I recalled those boiling, expanding gases of the convection regions, brilliantly writhing in continuous waves and branches of light, and the stupendous energy of the dense radiations emitted outward from the photosphere. Radiation is the process of transfer deep inside, the photoelectric process of bluish radiations. Here at the bottom of Earth's atmospheric ocean, these same radiations are filtered and diffused into a glowing light with the soft blue sky above.

Gone was the deep sadness of my parting from Akon. Instead, a great happiness and contentment filled my soul. I lived again through all the wonderful things he had said to me, the touch of his hands, the exciting, electric presence of such a gentle and possessive man. He was a man from another planet, another world—a real man, not just a figment of my imagination or a dream or a thought, but real. He was real, with as physical a body as anyone else on this planet. This stirring and wonderful contact with my beloved, whom I had known in my heart all my life, is the only real, tangible thing that has ever happened to me. Everything else in my daily life on Earth seems more like a dream to me. I feel I am not really a part of it, and therefore I must belong to Akon's dimension in space and time.

Perhaps there are many people living on Earth who have this same experience of the variable nature of space and time, and can move at will from one dimension to another, fully aware of the physical nature of both dimensions of matter and antimatter because they are harmonically attuned to both. The key to our existence in the universe is to be harmonically attuned to all things in nature. If one is attuned, one can take part in all things and be an active participant in the variable nature of the cosmos. In this way, one attains all knowledge and perception, and can eventually make physical contact with people beyond Earth's light barrier. My sister was aware of these truths, and was quietly content to accept the reality of Akon's presence in her environment. She was unaware of the future, and did not foresee the suddenness of her physical meeting with him, in the mist, on an evening to come.

As Akon had explained to me, there is a simple explanation for the fact that people from another planet are able to visit Earth if they wish to. Within the protection of their giant spaceships of light—the fantastic starships shaped like galaxies—they are completely safe and mobile.

Most Earth people are unable to understand the advanced physics of this alien science. Their minds are limited to the comprehension of their own narrow environment. Not for them the vast secrets of the universe and how the wave motion of light controls the destiny of humankind, its pulse wave creating the vast and everlasting waves of the oceans. Its spiral system encompasses the vast circumference and reaches of the galaxy in an everlasting creation of energy and matter. Its varying frequencies give us the nature of existence in matter and antimatter, creating stars, planets and people adapted to the surfaces of planets in varying frequencies of time. As the pulse of energy moves within the substance of land, rocks or earth, its pulse wave can be seen undulating across the solid landscape in the form of earthquakes perceptible to the frequency of our eyes.

I was brought back to the realization of Earth time by the Zulu maid bringing the early morning tea. She paused for a moment on her way out, her dark brown eyes wide and soft with devotion.

"You watched the sky wagon?" I gently asked in her own tongue.

"*Inkosikazi*, we have seen *umlingo*[1] wagon in the sky. We ran to hide in a *donga*[2], shielding our eyes from the brightness like the lightning. Our fathers told of such things coming out of the sky, and the *inyanga yezulu*[3]

---

1. *magic*
2. *deep ravine*
3. *storm doctor*

Flying Saucer Hill.

says he has seen them many times and has talked to them when they create a great black cloud with lightning and thunder."

She spoke with awe, hardly daring to talk about such things she could never understand.

"*Umthakathi*[1]," she said as she scurried through the door and fled to the kitchen.

Later in the morning, my sister and I mounted on two of the quietest mares and rode to the mountaintop. Where the great spaceship had landed, the long grass remained flattened in a vast circle. The horses refused to approach, but stood with their heads down, snorting and trembling in every limb. Sensing the alien presence, the old mare I was riding suddenly reared and turned on her hocks to flee, but I checked her and brought her down quietly with soothing words and reassuring hands. She stood quietly then, her nostrils flaring now and again as she snorted her defiance to the alien something that had left its scent on the veld.

The reactions of the mares made my sister very nervous, and she allowed her mount to shy away from the awesome circle of flattened grass.

"Were you not afraid, Elizabeth?" she asked. "How did you know and learn not to be afraid?"

Without waiting for an answer, she dismounted from her mare and gave the reins to an *umfana* who stood nearby, gaping at the flattened

---

1. *wizard, sorcerer or witch*

circle of veld. The small boy was so engrossed with what he saw that the mare easily jerked the reins from his hands and galloped away down the hill. My mare reared again in her attempt to follow, but I quieted her. I moved her away from the landing area and dismounted.

The whole neighborhood was there, squatting in the long grass on top of the mountain. The *amakhehla*[1] and *izalukazi*[2] were gesticulating wildly and talking at the top of their voices.

"I told you so!" they called. "Ladam foretold this. This mountain is *umlingo!*"

Leaving the mare with my sister, I stepped into the circle of flat grass. Standing in the center, I looked up into the depths of blue, into the far reaches of the sky and the fathomless seas of space, knowing the truth and the golden glory of love's light. The Zulu women began to chant, setting up a high-pitched wail and turning their faces to the heavens, calling on *Unkulunkulu*[3] to preserve for all time the hallowed mountain and the spot where the great wagon of the skies had landed.

"If only someone was here with a movie film, soundtrack and the lot," my sister called out in her practical way—and the spell was broken.

Zulu matrons and maidens stood up out of the long waving grass, and with graceful dignity moved off along the mountain path, their gaily beaded skirts swinging with the motion of their stride. The children ran on ahead, naked except for strings of beads. The married women wore colorful capes that blew in the wind and carried infants on their backs. Their heavy, clay-matted head adornments were done in distinctive styles peculiar to the district. The menfolk remained in hushed conclave, squatting on their haunches in the long grass, while the women and children returned to the semicircle of beehive-shaped huts on the lower slopes of the mountain.

Like a curved horn, the hut emplacement nestled on the northeastern slope. The long stems of grass, which made both the thatch of the roof and the walls tied to a shell of wattle, glistened in the morning sunlight. There was only one low entrance to each hut, shielded from the wind by a grass screen that was curved on a wooden frame and beaded in many

---

1. *old men*
2. *old women*
3. *God*

colors. The clay floors within were made of a mixture of fresh cow dung and earth.

Worshipping the spirits of their ancestors, who came from the heaven country, the Amazulu prepared to celebrate the return of the sky gods. Young men loped off into the veld, spreading the message to the distant kraals. They covered kilometers of rolling country with their easy, loping stride and drummed a *knobkierrie*[1] against the inner side of a hide shield.

The runaway mare was caught and returned to my sister. We mounted and rode slowly back to the homestead.

"When will Akon come back again?" my sister asked.

My heart missed a beat at the thought of next time. Would it be soon? The warmth of my love brought a flush to my cheeks, and I looked back to the mountaintop as I answered.

"It could be any time. We must just wait."

Back in the old farmhouse, we quietly discussed the subject as Muti came from the kitchen laden with a tray of delicious tea and freshly baked scones. He placed the tray on the table for us, and then retreated to hover in the shadows beyond the door, hoping to catch some of our conversation.

We Have Sent Our Best Reporters Over to Pretoria to See the Air Chief of Staff.

The Chief, anxiously awaiting news of me, sent an urgent telegram to ascertain my whereabouts. I dispatched a full report to him, and was happy to receive an excited and very encouraging letter in response. He stated that my news was of such vital import that he was flying out to South Africa to see me. Upon his arrival, we returned to the farm and spent many hours out on the mountaintop, while a lone Air Force Harvard droned and circled in the sky overhead. Flying Saucer Hill remained aloof, however, to all who came to peer and search for clues—as many people did, trespassing from the far road.

"What with all these people and the Air Force surveillance," the Chief said, "you will have to find another meeting place or wait a long time before you see Akon again."

---

1. *A stick with a knob at one end.*

"Let the hue and cry die down," he advised me before he returned to England. "People soon forget."

On my return to Johannesburg, flying-saucer enthusiasts questioned me and clamored for information as the fantastic story came out in the press. My training and powers of observation into human nature prevented me from laying all my facts bare, for these were not the people to confide in and tell of things beyond their comprehension. They were a motley crowd of cranks and self-seekers, some of them very vicious and dangerous, I thought.

Early in 1956, Johannesburg was a hotbed of flying-saucer intrigue. Societies flourished like fungi in the bracing warmth of the highveld summer, watered by the fanatical enthusiasm of many misguided individuals whose egotism far outweighed any good they attempted to do. Dogfights and bickering were the order of the day, and UFO research societies crumbled and withered through gross ignorance and vicious jealousy.

They shouted to the four winds that they were the experts. Only they were capable of making any statements about flying saucers. While they tried to steal the limelight for themselves, the situation steadily deteriorated. As the tempo of viciousness increased, I sensed how dearly they would love to revert to their natural instincts and burn me at the stake as a witch.

Then, suddenly, their tactics changed. I was threatened with abduction if I refused to hand over scientific details of the flying saucer and its propulsion systems. The danger to me and my family increased daily. Threatening telephone calls and letters made our lives increasingly difficult and fraught with danger, even in our own home. How dare they! I thought. Because I was living alone with my children in a cottage in Parktown, they thought I would be easy bait to snatch and hold. I appealed to the authorities for protection, and they responded with prompt and very effective action. An ex-policeman was detailed to guard my home, and from then on I was never allowed to go anywhere by myself. It was wonderful to have peace and not be threatened anymore. The days passed and the weather was perfect as it can be only on the highveld. My daughter studied for her medical degree at the university just down the road, and my son attended day school.

Then one day events changed again, dramatically, as the Air Force appeared, sweeping across the mackerel sky in a wide swathe. High above, a great spaceship hovered at nineteen thousand meters of altitude, flashing in the morning sunlight. The jets, scrambled from Waterkloof Air Force Base to investigate, were unable to climb above fourteen thousand meters. They swept away to the north in battle formation, leaving long, tenuous vapor trails. The wide open sky retained the tranquillity of eternity and the silent watcher high above remained—a circular starship, glowing and flashing high above the cirrocumulus.

Indifferent to the excitement and consternation in the great city sprawling over the Ridge of White Waters, the silent watcher remained, glowing within her light field. Filled with wonder and awe, thousands of people watched and waited. Fear of the unknown entered many hearts, and the condensation trails of the fighter jets hung across the higher atmosphere like the wing feathers of the wind.

Suddenly, out of the depths of space, another starship appeared. The two ships remained hovering, moving gently from side to side and up and down for a time. Then one of them made off to the south at great speed and vanished. The second great spaceship lowered a little in the clear noonday sky and then vanished also, as suddenly as it had appeared.

My heart filled with joy as I watched from the spacious garden of a friend. Akon was back—and he had contacted my mind through the ether of the heavens. The warmth of his love coursed through my whole being and filled my soul with a sudden glow. My body stirred to the glory of his presence as the ocean is stirred by the winds of a heavenly calm, and the golden rays of love poured the radiance of the universe into my eyes as I gazed into the depths of blue from whence he came.

Noting the radiance in my face, my friends questioned me about the spaceship. I told them it was Akon's ship, and that I would now have to go back to the mountains. Taking my leave of them, I quickly drove my MG out of the drive and back down the hill to my cottage.

The shrill and strident urgency of the telephone greeted my homecoming, and I answered it.

"Elizabeth! A flying saucer over Johannesburg! What do you know—never seen anything like it. There is bedlam here in the newspaper offices!"

I could hear a babble of voices from the other end of the telephone.

"What a row!" I answered. "I can't hear anything you say now. You will have to shout."

"We have sent our best reporters over to Pretoria to see the Air Chief of Staff. Are you going to the farm, Elizabeth? What is happening?"

"I'm sure it will all be on the radio," I said. "You must listen in. Bye, now. I have to go."

I put the receiver down and told my son to pack for the farm, including warm clothes. Then I went to my writing desk to await my sister's call. The previous evening, I remembered, had been quiet and perfect. A waxing moon had nudged up beyond the clouds on the eastern horizon. The green wealth of trees and shrubs that flowed down the hill swayed gently in a fresh wind from the east. From the zoo, the peacocks called, their plaintive notes swelling with the wind—a warning of storms to come.

I noted that the sky had now cleared; even the high cirrus had gone. A cold front would come up later from the south, however. Instinctively, I looked into the sky. I could tell by reading its sheen that a change of weather was coming.

The telephone trilled again, an urgent summons, and my sister's voice came through, clear and perfect. "Come immediately, my dear," she said. "And watch the weather."

"We are leaving now."

Akon would be there, I thought. My heart sang a paean of joy.

"Ready?" I asked my son. "Let's go."

"Right, Mom." David's excited voice answered from the depths of a jersey as he pulled it over his head. "Take Susan to the MG, and I'll bring Vicki."

Susan was already waiting at the door. Her fine, intelligent head was cocked to one side as she watched and listened to everything. Bred through the centuries to guard and protect, her golden body stiffened with the majesty and awareness of the collie. Vicki heard every word too. She scurried out of the kitchen with her mouth still full of food, her short corgi legs hardly able to propel her into the MG's back seat. Susan, meanwhile, waited with haughty dignity to step in after us.

The mist swept up over the mountains of Natal as a cold front came in from the south, bearing the fragrance of moisture and shrouding the beauty of the hills. As we came to the fork in the road leading from the family home in the valley to my sister's farm over the mountain, I shifted the MG slowly into second gear to take the slippery mountain track. The car moved smoothly and powerfully over the rough track to the boundary gate.

As we stopped, I heard the distant rumble of thunder, and my heart missed a beat. Be calm, I said to myself. Keep your cool. The nearby trees loomed and swayed in the wind, and the dark mass of Flying Saucer Hill seemed remote and forbidding through the scudding mist of clouds. Again we heard the ominous sound of thunder, sudden and lengthening from incessant lightning.

I showed an outward calm as I called to David to hurry with the gate, but my heart began to beat wildly with the approach of the storm. The wind suddenly died, and as a meteorologist, I instantly recognized a muffled roar. Caught out on the windward side of the mountain, our chance of survival would be slim indeed. Shifting the MG into first gear, I nursed her gradually up and up the long, wet, muddy track—slowly, so slowly, the powerful engine responding to my quiet and gentle handling—until at last we topped the mountain and slowly descended to the homestead nestled on the northeast slopes.

An icy southwest gale ripped through the pines beside the track. As I drove into the long garage beside the farmhouse, a hailstone the size of a cricket ball hit the ground beside the MG and bounced up again through the farmhouse's kitchen window with a crash of shattering glass. In that

David and the MG that went aboard the spaceship.

second of ominous vacuum, I hooted three times and Muti opened the door into the house. The lamp in his hand flared up the blackened glass in the wind sweeping through the garage. A barrage of hail blotted out all communication.

My sister's face, white and drawn, appeared over Muti's shoulder. As I stepped into the house, she put her arms around me and David in thanksgiving. She gathered us all into the drawing room and poured us cups of hot, delicious tea. Without a word, we sat and enjoyed the tea and buttered scones. Outside, the dreadful chaos and shattering roar of the storm went on and on.

Susan and Vicki sat huddled against my legs, Susan's sensitive ears twitching at each shift in the storm's fury. My sister's dogs and cats huddled together under the Bechstein grand piano. We heard the hail and the shifting wind destroying the unguarded windows on the northeast side of the house. Lightning struck with a deafening roar as it destroyed the old iron-bark gum on the sloping lawn, its bole riven to the ground.

As the awful din lessened, my sister shouted across the tea table. "Thank heavens you made it! Jock's caught in the stable. They sheltered all the horses and cows just in time."

In the wake of the terrible storm, hundreds of birds lay dead and dying. They had been caught in the uneasy hush before the onslaught. We turned the warmth of the kitchen into a casualty ward for the limp feathered bodies, laying them in baskets. We scoured through the garden and beyond, into the fields, gathering up broken bodies. A misty rain continued in the aftermath of the hostile cloud, and writhing veils of vapor ascended from the ice-covered ground. Many trees were uprooted. Others stood limp and battered, or riven and shattered by lightning. The lovely garden—full of choice and exotic blooms, and so dear to my sister—was gone.

The Glory of My Awakening Spread Its Warmth through My Soul, and I Sensed Balanced Harmony.

Away to the west, the setting sun broke through the clouds over the peaks of the Drakensberg. As the clearcut cumulus head of the storm moved away to the north, the orange-red rays of the sun picked out the glowing surface of a spaceship. It hovered in the ice-blue sky, between the towering thunderheads and the ragged mist that tore across the lower reaches with the south wind.

"Akon's ship is here," I called out, slipping on the hail in my haste to reach my sister's side. I stood with her and we watched the sky with bated breath as an enormous, wraithlike ship appeared above the towering thunderheads. It was the mothership, hovering in the darkening sky. I caught my breath with wonder as it slowly lowered toward the Earth, its gigantic sides glistening with an unearthly radiance. Never before had the mothership come so low over the mountains.

A deep longing filled my heart, and a strange foreboding spread its wings through my mind. The mothership had returned as promised, and Pleia would be there. Akon was safely back, but the mothership had also come to say goodbye—goodbye to Earth and her peoples of strange and violent ways. It would now go back to its home system, away from the dangers of the Sun's system. Time was running out for the planets of the Sun's system, which were heading toward their destiny of violence as they have done in the past.

Jock came up from the stables, sliding and slipping over the hail, and kissed me.

"I thought you would be aware of that dangerous cloud buildup, and that you would get here before it," he said quietly. "But I wish they, up there in the spaceship, could prevent vicious clouds like that from forming."

My sister's joy, though, was overwhelming as she put her arm about Jock and watched the spaceship as it lowered still more into the darkening sky. Jock's face was a study in careful observation mixed with a sense of wonder as he watched the spaceship. A military man, an officer of high repute, he was suddenly confronted with the truth. He was the cleanest-living person I had ever known, with a fantastic gentleness and humanity rare in such a high-ranking military man. He was always thoughtful and considerate of others—a trait inherited from his Scottish ancestors. He was indeed a link with the people in the spaceship.

Muti and the grooms stood by in utter silence, watching. Slowly, the great spaceship moved up again toward the heavens, aglow with its propulsion force. Then suddenly it was gone, back into the far reaches of the sky.

"I must go to the mountaintop," I said. "Akon will be there."

Before they could answer, I was on my way back to the house to get a jersey. The cold south wind whipped about me as I stood on the summit, but I did not have to wait long. A blue-white sphere appeared out of the dark, star-studded sky, and Akon's spaceship silently hovered close to the ground and gently landed. I reached the spaceship as Akon stepped through the automatic door. Jumping to the ground, he gathered me up in his arms and carried me into the warmth of the cabin, and the cold wind of a changing climate was shut out.

Akon buried his face in my hair, whispering, "My beloved. My very own, my life, my precious woman. The seas of space will never part us, as our thoughts are forever united in the far distances of the sky. We are given this privilege of life, this electric essence to fuse and become one in the everlasting cycle of light. Our love is the divine essence of life, whereby the soul awakens to knowledge in the higher spheres. The universe sanctions our union."

The glory of my awakening spread its warmth through my soul, and I sensed the balanced harmony of this everlasting lease we sense as life. In that moment, the secret of life was revealed to me in the golden rays of Akon's love, but a moment later a clattering noise through the viewing lens disturbed our peace. Turning to the lens, we watched an Air Force helicopter land nearby in the projected beam of a searchlight. Akon immediately went to the control desk and pressed a button at one end of the panel. The spaceship vibrated with a high-pitched hum that sounded faintly beyond her double walls.

"I do not wish to parley with military men. This is not the reason for my landing on Earth." Akon sounded annoyed, and for the first time I saw him frown. "The field of my ship has now been intensified. We are now invisible to their line of vision, owing to the bending of the light rays. I think the Air Force is aware of this trick, however. Before they come any closer, my beloved, and get harmed by these field differentials, I shall take you back to the homestead."

We landed in the field beside the shattered garden. Through the hedge, I saw a light in my sister's bedroom—she would be anxious and waiting up for me. The mist had come down again like a white drape over everything.

Akon carried me out of the spaceship, moving swiftly over the slippery hail. Glancing down, I realized that he was not walking but gliding over the top of it all with smooth, uncanny swiftness. Before I could say anything, we were on the front stoep of the farmhouse. My sister came to the door, and gasped as she saw Akon's tall figure glowing in the dim light from the fabric of his close-fitting garment.

"It's all right," we said. "It's only us."

Akon immediately went to her and kissed her on both cheeks.

"Whatever happens, never be afraid," he said to her. "Soon you will come to us. You are too frail and gentle for this world, which breeds a robust and earthy people devoid of higher knowledge."

Turning to me, he held me close in his arms and kissed the top of my head. "The heights of Cathkin," he whispered.

Swiftly, he turned and glided away into the mist. I caught a glimpse of a gravity belt around his waist before he disappeared into the fog. Straining our eyes toward the field, we could see nothing. The ship had moved into another dimension of time, into the higher octaves in the spectrum of light.

"Come," my sister May breathed. "That was the most wonderful moment of my life." She put her arm around my shoulders, took me into the kitchen and gave me a steaming mug of hot milk.

There was a loud clattering noise outside. Running to a window, I was just in time to see the Air Force helicopter land on the lawn in the light of its searchlight.

"Two Air Force Officers Are Observing Us Very Closely from the Rim of the Dip with Binoculars."

A knock on the door disturbed Jock, who was sitting beside the fire reading and listening to the radio. He turned off the radio, muttering about it doing funny things, as he went to answer the knock. A few moments later he came into the kitchen.

"We have some Air Force types who have lost their way in the mist and decided to come down rather than go on in this thick fog," he said. "Can we make them some hot tea?"

After making them comfortable in front of the log fire in the drawing room, I heard Jock say to them, "You chaps still looking for the spaceships?"

"We were alerted, sir, to look for flying saucers in this area," answered the young captain.

"Well," said Jock, "they have been over this area. I observed the big one myself, soon after that killer storm. I will give you all the information I have—but perhaps my sister-in-law may agree to help."

The captain looked startled when he turned and saw me pouring out the tea, and both young men became strangely silent.

"You chaps look done in," Jock said. "No need to be afraid of Liz—and as for the chap in the spaceship, he is just like one of us, only far more evolved. Just leave Liz alone, that's all. This is her own private affair, and has nothing to do with the Air Force. I know, I know, violating our air space and all that. Unless she decided to cooperate with you, though, there is nothing you can do. But leave her alone now, I'm warning you. She may answer your questions in a day or two."

"Yes, Jock is right," I said. "In a few days' time, I will speak to you. I am tired now and wish to go to bed. Good night."

The two officers stood up. They saluted with such precision that I felt highly honored and said so.

"You chaps had better doss down here for the night," Jock told them. "Radio the blokes in the sky and tell them to go home and cut out the noise up there. Things are going to happen. We are living in momentous times, a part of history vital for our country."

The captain looked relieved and saluted again.

"Thank you, sir," he said, and, turning smartly, he opened the door and went out into the white fog to his helicopter. Tendrils of mist blew into the warm room through the half-open door—the eternal mist of the mountains had cut visibility to nil.

"Just as well there's a wide expanse of flat lawn out there," I remarked. "Enough room to maneuver a battleship on."

"The captain must have observed it well during daylight when he was reconnoitering the summit of Flying Saucer Hill," May replied. "I watched them circling in the helicopter over the area this morning while you were on your way here. They are pretty clued up on your movements. I must say, it's wonderful to be under the wing of the Air Force."

"Well," I sighed as I climbed into bed. "There's a reason for it."

The next morning dawned with a beauty of unparalleled clarity after the storm of the day before. The mist had cleared away, and the long slopes of grassland leading to the summit of Flying Saucer Hill stretched away before me. The rolling green foothills beyond sparkled in the clear and cold atmosphere, alive within a mantle of singing grass that bowed and waved in velvet rhythm to the breath of the south wind. It shined and rippled as the sunlight reflected on every blade.

Scattered farms lay in the valleys, and in the sheltered vale beyond the hill, the gracious old house of my childhood days nestled among the trees. In the sky, a lone Harvard kept its solitary vigil, droning and circling to maintain Air Force reconnaissance.

The sky is a great ocean of air, moving restlessly over our heads, a canopy of protection against the radiation beyond and a fragile thing of beauty and turbulence between us and the vast reaches of space. Earth moves in timeless rhythm, in vulnerable faith, around the Sun. The fathomless reaches press against her surface and the planet's inhabitants, like deep-sea fishes, adapt themselves to the pressure of their environment. Earth is alone and vulnerable, forever in orbit around the Sun, whose light reflects a delicate blue sheen from Earth's surface like a beacon of hope in the void.

Lying in the long singing grass on the top of the hill, I sensed the changing rhythm of time, and I knew Akon was near. There was a rushing in the grass, and Vicki nuzzled my face. Panting with satisfaction at finding me after following my scent, she lay down flat on her tummy with her short hind legs stretched out behind, cooling off and panting her happiness. Then she sat up, sniffed the wind and whined, her ears alert and waiting. Her great brown eyes softened and focused, and in a flash, I knew.

Turning and looking up, I saw my beloved standing tall against the blue of sky, looking down at me with that wonderful expression of gentle love. Taking my hand in his, he helped me to my feet. We laughed together as we went down into the dip, where the beautiful ship of light rested on the ground.

The shining spaceship was exotic and unearthly. I stopped, spellbound, filled with wonder and awe at the proximity of such a ship and what it meant to me. My hand trembled in Akon's as the wonder of it all impressed my mind with indelible clarity, and I looked at Akon standing tall beside me, his eyes loving and tender and a gentle smile creasing his clearcut features. My mind imprinted forever his tall lithe form, the fine strength of his face, his hair, the high forehead, his every expression.

"Yes, my beloved, it is all real, very real, and I am real too," he whispered, and gathered me up in his arms. He stepped onto the hull of his spaceship, passed through the doorway and placed me on the soft bench inside the cabin. Then he returned for Vicki, who made herself quite at home sniffing round the cabin, until her quick canine mind told her it was bad manners and she lay down with a guilty look in her eyes. Akon gave her a fig, and she ate it with an air of the utmost devotion, watching him all the time with her soft brown eyes.

"We have other visitors outside," Akon remarked. "Two Air Force officers are observing us very closely from the rim of the dip, with binoculars. I saw them before I carried you into the ship. You were so completely absorbed with wonder, my dear, that I did not wish to startle or upset you. Now, we depart instantly to the high plateau of Cathkin, where we shall not be disturbed anymore."

Akon approached the circular wall, and a door slid open.

"Come, my beloved," he said. "Within you will find a change of clothing. Your shoes are wet from the grass on the hill, and you will feel more comfortable if you relax now."

He turned back to the control panel as I rose and passed through the doorway and into a narrow, curved cabin that was part of the dome. Sunlight streamed in through the portholes onto the rose-red carpeting. Long double mirrors between the ports reflected my movements as I entered. On the right side of the cabin a raised platform merged with the curved wall. It was covered in shimmering silk of the same glorious rose-red color as the carpet, and at the other end of the long cabin a sunken bath glowed like mother-of-pearl, giving out a light of its own. Beside it stood a low, comfortable lavatory seat, its base glowing like the bath and the seat made of a smooth rose material. I relaxed immediately as I absorbed the beauty and harmony of the reflected vibration of rose and gold from the glowing light of mother-of-pearl walls.

How delightful it was to take off my gillie shoes, the thick tartan kilt and hot twin set, and stand naked in the glorious and invigorating atmosphere of the spaceship. There was an elusive perfume like the tang of the sea wind. Going to the sunken bath, I pressed a golden disk set in the pearl wall of the bath. Instantly, green foaming water gurgled up. Startled, I pressed another disk to stop it, but a fine shower landed on my head. When

I pressed a third disk, the shower stopped and the foaming water surged to a stop just below the rim and automatically lowered through a run-out below the rim. Stepping down, I reveled in the cool, delicious water—it was soft, green and foamy, with a velvety smoothness against my skin. There was a mild taste of salt in it. I sensed that the abundance of minerals in the water must hold some secret ingredients to keep one healthy and increase lifespan, while its cleansing properties made soap unnecessary.

The water was lovely, but I eventually stepped out of the bath. I wondered how I could dry myself, but as I left the tub, soft, warm air blew against my skin. Soon I was dry, my skin soft, silky and smooth, with that lovely, elusive perfume like the tang of the sea wind.

Standing naked before the mirrors, I found a silver-mounted hairbrush. Taking down my long, golden hair, I brushed it out to dry after the shower. There was movement in the mirrors. Without a sound, Akon came behind me and put his hands into my hair, tumbling it up against his face and burying his lips into its mass. Holding me close to him, he removed a ring from his little finger and placed it over my middle finger. It was exotic and beautiful, made of beaten silver and green enamel with a great stone of light set in the middle.

"It is too large for you, my beloved one. So we will place a half band of silver within it. I want you to wear it always as a part of me, to maintain our telepathic communication for all time."

Akon's ring.

I could feel and sense the magic properties emanating from the ring. Akon put his hand under my chin, tilting my head up and back, and he kissed me with a long and lingering kiss on the lips. Picking me up in his arms, he carried me to the silken platform by the curved wall. Its firm softness supported our bodies with luxurious comfort, as I gave myself to the man from outer space.

"My beloved, my life," Akon whispered again and again, as I surrendered in ecstasy to the magic of his lovemaking. Our bodies merged in magnetic union as the divine essence of our spirits became one, and in doing so I became whole.

As our bodies became one, the fusion of the electric essence of life was attained, and the ensuing ecstasy and balance of electrical forces transcended all things experienced in life. To love and be loved, encompassed within the magnetic emotion of mind and body in perfect union of affinities—my beloved swept me away into the reality and I found the true meaning of love in mating with a man from another planet. How beautiful is nature's plan to mate in love and harmony, the joy of the soul, spirit and body—the three-in-one transcended into timelessness. We lived for one another in the consummation of the soul within the rapturous ecstasy of fulfilled love.

The eternal magic of wholeness bonded our love with the everlasting light of the universe, and I sensed an awareness I had not been conscious of before as I lay in Akon's arms. I sensed the life and continuous movement within each tiny particle of air, a thrilling awareness and knowledge of the whole, of magnetism, the essence and stuff of life. To become whole oneself is to find that magic lease we sense as life.

The pulse of life throbbed through the air, in ways I had not really been aware of before. The living planet beneath our spaceship, as we rested on the high plateau of Cathkin, is a living breathing entity, creating continuous life and movement. It harbors this life within its nebulous blue atmosphere as it moves like a spaceship through the fathomless reaches of space, and only Earth's children can preserve its frailty. Throughout intergalactic space, on the surface of other planets, other Earths, it is the same. All are relative, all have the magnetic stuff of life and all are within the whole.

Akon lifted me gently from the soft couch. My hair, a tumbled mass of gold, partially concealed my body as he brushed it back and piled it up on my head, binding it with a golden cord. Trembling before the mirrors, I watched his gentle hands manipulate my hair, coiling and twisting the gold fabric through it until it was firmly up in a beautiful classic style. How wonderful was this deep consideration and care—how wonderful to feel and to know our precious unity, the spiritual and physical union so complete that we can care for each other's needs as one.

On a low stool beside the mirrors, I saw a gown, diaphanous and lovely, the color of deep rose. Akon bent down and took the gown from the stool. He placed it around my shoulders, pressing the front edges together, and it immediately hung to my ankles in delicate folds without seams of any kind. My body gleamed through the thin, chiffonlike material, and the round neckline and long sleeves fit loosely and comfortably with a featherlike softness. My feet remained bare, free of any covering on the firm, springy carpet.

"The recurring pattern of our lives has now fused for us in this point of time, my beloved one," Akon said gently as we moved together through the doorway into the larger cabin. "The true purpose of mating is not only for the reproduction of offspring, but to retain and satisfy opposite forces of electricity so that these elements may fuse and retain nature's balance between the sexes. One is not balanced without the other, and it is because Earth men misunderstand these truths that there is so much suffering, ignorance and primitive superstition and fear regarding sex. The purpose of mating is not to have biological offspring alone—mating is forever, to retain the balanced whole between male and female. Each is necessary and vital to the other. Magnetic attraction and mating by natural selection has a beneficial effect on the forming mind of the unborn child.

"The haphazard, often aggressive mating associated with procreation on Earth is a direct result of aggressive and warlike tendencies inherited within the forming mind of the unborn. Violence is an inherited instinct, and humankind on Earth have it in full measure. How wrong is their concept, whereby to become holy in the eyes of their God, they must become celibate in mind and body. How narrow and ignorant are their ways. Only the pure in heart shall see the universe. The spark that creates the divine soul is born in the mating and union of male and female in perfect love and harmony, as our child shall be.

"Our affinities and loved ones are found through natural telepathy—and distance, as you know, is no barrier whatsoever."

Akon talked on as we went toward the wall on the opposite side of the main cabin. A door slid open at our approach to reveal another cabin like the rest cabin, following the curve of the dome. Glorious colors filled the cabin in restful harmony, with the same springy rose-red carpeting that was a delight to my bare feet.

"This is the kitchen, where we grow our sustenance and relax to enjoy it," Akon said.

Curved along the wall were long crystal cupboards, filled with liquid and bathed in a radiance of soft blue electric light. Fresh vegetables and fruits were actually growing within—emerald leaves and colorful and exotic fruits added their natural vibrations of glorious color to the blue radiance. At one end of the cabin, a mass of beautifully scented flowers grew in natural profusion among other plants with gaily colored leaves. Like anemones with their bright and different colors, the flowers seemed to live and vibrate as the satin sheen of each petal glowed with a light of its own.

At the other end of the cabin, a table and sink gleamed. Light emanated from it, and from the walls and ceiling, as if the whole cabin was alight with soft, natural sunlight. The ceiling, a dome of deep blue sky, was like the natural sky of a planet, giving the impression of infinite distance. Running my hand over the sink, I noticed that it was made of thick mother-of-pearl. It too gleamed with its own light, alive with a deep pink glow.

At the table we prepared a delicious meal of fresh, uncooked vegetables and fruit mixed with tasty herbs, nuts of all kinds and a dressing made from a creamy substance filled with aromatic spices. Fresh fruit juices and a sparkling wine complimented the meal. We reclined on a low, soft platform by the wall, sipping wine from long-stemmed rose-red crystals.

"I'm happy we do not have to live on pills, or dehydrated or tinned foods of any kind," I remarked. "This is simply delicious."

"Of course not," Akon said. "We enjoy natural foods and wines. We have the knowledge and scientific means to do so."

He stroked my cheek with the back of his hand as we reclined in restful silence. There was no need for incessant chatter. Akon and his race were never voluble. Quiet telepathic communication was all that was necessary, and it was quite natural for me to be a part of this lovely relaxing silence. In fact, I gradually became aware that I really did belong to this civilization, and that I had been planted on Earth as a child, to be brought up by a family on Earth in whom there was no resemblance to me whatsoever.

We lay together and finished the tasty meal, using one bowl between us and smooth wooden spoons. When we got up, we rinsed the three utensils in the sink in the green foamy water with the fragrance of the sea, and we put them away in the places provided underneath.

"Where is Sheron?" I asked.

"He went off early this morning to collect the various indigenous plants and grasses that abound in these mountains to add to our interplanetary gardens on the home planet. He will return shortly."

"Are you also a botanist, my beloved?" I asked, wonderingly. "I notice how all the plants here in the spaceship respond to your hands. I could actually see them growing again after we picked some for salad."

"Indeed, yes. The love and care of all flora and fauna on the planets of our galaxy is of paramount importance to us, and I am in charge of the sciences of exobiology and botany, besides my duties as a specialist in variable stars."

Sheron came through from the large central cabin with a pouch of plant roots. Greeting me with a happy smile, he placed the roots in the sink and washed them well in a chemical solution taken from a container on the floor. He then put them away into a separate cupboard of clear crystal, where I saw the roots immediately branch out into natural growing positions within the liquid.

"You will notice new shoots sprouting within the irradiated liquid," Sheron said to me. "Now, to regulate growth to their natural speed as Earth specimens."

He adjusted a dial over the container, and the plant roots quivered and started to lengthen. Pale green shoots burst out from the top of the plants, then settled down to normal growth as their time frequency regulated. They looked very healthy and virile, floating in the blue liquid and forming themselves to their natural shape as they would grow in the soil of Earth.

We relaxed with Sheron while he prepared a meal for himself and discussed how the people of Earth were struggling to reach into space with rockets. The answer to all their problems, I thought, was landed here on the high plateau at the base of Cathkin Peak—a beautiful spaceship of light, resting in the swaying grasses that sang in the wind of the glory of the universe, while the mountains of the Dragon lay sleeping against the tranquil sky. Only the high-pitched whistle of an Air Force jet disturbed the remote quiet.

Radiation from the Earth and the cosmos gives vital nonphysical forces to plants. These forces are absorbed by all flora and fauna. They are vital and necessary to all life. Certain geological positions on the surface of Earth interact harmonically to generate this unseen life factor, which is the energy of pure cosmic radiation. People who are aware of this can find these areas on the surface of this planet, and thereby benefit their health and longevity. Plants will grow in healthy profusion because the atmosphere around them is irradiated with cosmic energy as the four forces of the universe, or the unified field, is channeled through the area. A four-sided pyramid will channel cosmic energy in the same way, if it is aligned correctly on a geometric position in harmonic interaction with light or the star of a system.

To penetrate the secrets of nature is very simple, because we are a part of nature ourselves. We are all born out of stardust, spawned in the transformation of material from interstellar dust, which takes place continuously. All life is one, not only on Earth but beyond it also. The chain of life of each one of us stretches back, unbroken, to its very beginning in the galaxy, as each of us shares with other beings and other humans on other worlds a common ancestor descended from a dust cloud. Nature gives us a simple scientific explanation for all things and all life if we can interact in harmony with all things in nature and become one with the galaxy in which we have our being.

Akon had chosen the heights of Cathkin for its geological position on the surface of Earth, where cosmic energy is channeled through the planet and the surrounding atmosphere is energized. Only on these geological areas will Akon land his spaceship for any length of time. In this way, I was able to find him and we were able to come together in the time field of Earth.

"That is so," Sheron said, answering my thoughts. "There are other specimens of plants growing on the eastern slope of this mountain, and I shall go and get them now."

He went out through the central cabin and back to the soil of Earth, as the Sun glinted from his chestnut hair.

I looked up into Akon's eyes and felt mesmerized as he willed me to move toward him. I did so, and he picked me up like a feather and carried me back into the rest cabin. The door silently sealed behind us.

Gently he opened my gown and it slipped from my body to the floor.

"How white your skin is," he whispered, placing me down on the silken platform, and he kissed my body from the top of my head to the tips of my toes. I swooned in that moment of ecstasy when I felt Akon's naked body press into mine as he made love to me again with such complete possession. The wonderful abandonment of giving myself to him and becoming one with him was a sublime happiness as we lay together in union of physical bodies, our spiritual energy in complete harmony.

What a wonderful way to conceive! Surely, there could be nothing more beautiful than this. The child to come would be the living evidence of perfect love and harmony—brought forth in happiness and perfect fusion, a fantastic inheritance to impart to the future generations of his race. We drifted off into peaceful slumber, the most glorious sleep I have ever experienced.

"WHAT WILL HAPPEN WHEN I GIVE BIRTH TO YOUR CHILD?"

Akon gently awakened me and I stretched, utterly relaxed in the peace and quiet of the spaceship. Placing the lovely gown about my body again, Akon pressed it together and it became one piece without seams. I sat up and looked out of the porthole, and found the answers to life in that unguarded moment of relaxation as I tuned in and became one with the universe—for calmness of mind and serenity of character is the flowering of the soul, and spiritual strength and equanimity the hallmark of advancement.

Instinctively I turned to advancing my soul toward light energy to move with the magnetic field into timelessness, wisdom and love. The everlasting life force, the great intelligence of the universe, is contacted through the forces of light, and only a balanced outlook and understanding can clear the way for development within the mind, where light is born of timelessness.

"Light is sought by all human beings," Akon said, replying to my thoughts. "Through eons of time they have turned their eyes to the light of the heavens. In this way only can they find the answers to all their problems—within the simplicity of light vibrations. To harness the natural forces of light is still beyond the comprehension of humankind, for this is an alien science that strikes at the very roots and foundations of their basic concepts. The limits of their knowledge reside within their bigger and better laboratories where experiments continually take place, probing and seeking the answers to the riddle of the universe in which they live. They do not find the answers, of course, because it is necessary to use the whole universe as a laboratory.

"To be efficient about the things that really matter in research, it is necessary to be inefficient about the things that do not matter so much, such as bigger and better laboratories, where inspiration and greatness are submerged within the surrounding efficiency of construction and personnel. They are like the great cathedrals, constructed to wipe the brains of humankind clean of every thought, and to subject them instead to the ways of earthbound religions, where people are led like so many sheep through the devious laws made by men of Earth.

"The material predominates because of man's striving for existence. In so doing, man treads brutally on his fellow men. The impatient atmosphere of humankind's striving will continue until they find the way through the light barrier. We cannot change their minds so rapidly. They have to learn through dire experience before their attitude of mind can change for the better. We cannot parley with them yet. We can only set an example and hope they will follow in times to come. Indeed, there are now many people across this planet who are changing, picking up our thoughts and attitude of mind through telepathic communication. Some of them are conscious of their contact with us, while others are unaware of the source affecting their change in outlook.

"You, my dear, are a very positive source for changing the attitude of mind of many people upon planet Earth. You are planting the seeds of knowledge, and in time many of these seeds will take root within the minds of humankind.

"People of Earth will remain in a state of turmoil and unease for another two decades before they will change and learn to respect the environment of their planet and understand the nature of the universe in which they live.

"No people of low cultural development are able to settle their differences around the conference table. They will always resort to the primitive method of intertribal rivalry and violence. Ruthless political domination holds sway, and spiritual values are swept aside and destroyed.

Civilizations can only lead their people when they have attained superior intelligence and spiritual advancement. Only a cultural background that has taken centuries to evolve can give time for the evolution of the mind and soul.

"From the safety and strength that the conquest of space affords to a civilization, we shall be able to direct and guide the course of events on Earth. This is our universal educational plan—we aim to retain the balance of slow evolution and positive thoughts. We ourselves cannot coexist and mix with these races. If we did, our gentle way of life would be overwhelmed and swamped by the more numerous and ruthless people who swarm on the surface of Earth. It will be a long process for human-kind to evolve, and there are many factors attached to this advancement within our galaxy. We are the guardians of our destiny, as we are the guardians of millions of other human beings evolving on other planets throughout the Milky Way galaxy, and we wish to retain the balance and harmony of all life."

Silently, Sheron came through to the control desk, and I knew things were going to happen.

"Couldn't the United States and Russia pinpoint our position here?" I asked. "We are in Earth time and very vulnerable."

"Indeed," Akon said as he pressed the light control button. I heard again that fantastic vibration from outside the ship as it smoothly slipped into its own time dimension. "You are right, my dear. We can depend on your powers of perception now. A Russian satellite is giving our exact position while a monitoring apparatus installed at Shirley Bay is giving out signals as it picks up our field differentials."

"We are too valuable a prize," said Sheron. "These nations have tried for years to capture us and spent millions of their money on the means to achieve this. Above all, they want our propulsion system and will do anything in their power to get it."

Earth scientists were now closing in with their magnetic probes, clos-ing in around this beautiful spaceship of light. It was invisible to the seek-ing eyes of men and radar, but not to the magnetic probe from Shirley Bay, nor to a Vostok in orbit with a crew of three.

"Earth-constructed flying saucers have been brought to ground," explained Akon, "and their secrets probed by scientists when they crashed back to the surface of Earth. This has caused much confusion among the peoples of Earth. But the propulsion systems of these crafts are not for space travel, only for atmospheric flight. As it will take another two decades before the people of Earth begin to change and respect their environment within the galaxy, they cannot yet understand the meaning of electrogravitic propulsion systems."

I saw the summit of Flying Saucer Hill and the far valleys beyond through the viewing lens. Without a word, I went through to the toilet cabin to change back into my clothes. They had dried out, and they felt soft and light with that same exotic fragrance like the tang of the sea wind. There was a soft vibration beyond the sealed walls of the spaceship, and I knew we were visible again in Earth time vibration—back in the frequency of this planet to enable me to step down to the soil of Earth again.

Akon held me close in his arms, and Sheron's cheerful smile and comforting assurance eased my devastating loneliness at our parting. To leave this wonderful atmosphere, to leave the magic presence and closeness of Akon, my beloved . . . I saw a gentle smile flit for a moment to light his ascetic face as he shared my thoughts. How beautiful, though, this true affinity filled with happiness and excitement, which overcame all feelings of despair or loneliness and gave instead a surge of strength and determination to live out one's true destiny.

Relaxed and content, I stepped out onto the hull of the spaceship with Akon. Vicki followed us back to the surface of the planet with a reluctance and droop of her ears, sitting sadly in the grass with her head held to one side as if wondering what would happen next. Akon held my face up to him between his big, gentle hands and looked long and deep into my eyes.

"I love you, my beloved," he whispered. "Distance is no barrier to thought or images, and I shall return."

"I love you with my whole being," I whispered back. "What will happen when I give birth to your child?"

The warmth of this thought spread its wings through my body, causing me to tremble.

"I shall be back to fetch you and claim my son. He is one of us, my beloved, my life. He is not of Earth."

He kissed me tenderly with the magic of his lips before turning away and jumping onto the hull of his ship. Then he was gone, the doorway closing—closing with inexorable finality behind his tall and straight figure.

LIFE IS ELECTRICITY, AND HOW FEW ARE BORN WITH THEIR AWAKENING CONSCIOUSNESS AWARE OF THE MAGIC LEASE WE SENSE AS LIFE.

Gathering Vicki up in my arms, I turned and ran to a safe distance from the spaceship, and then stood to watch it take off from the soil of Earth as the mist swept down over the mountain. The ship glowed with an unearthly radiance in the gloom of lowering mist. Its surface vibrated with light and it was gone. I stood alone with Vicki in the wet grass, and the south wind whipped my kilt and tore at my hair. Only the great circle of flattened grass remained. It would grow again in time with the first rain, imbued with a vigor and depth of green unknown elsewhere on Earth, thanks to the electric life-giving force generating vital properties within the soil beneath.

Walking back to the homestead, my whole being sang a paean of joy as the singing grasses on the mountainside sang a paean to the universe in the breath of the south wind. The glory of love and life enfolded me within its warmth, and I felt the wonder of the future. Vicki ran on ahead through the long grass. She put up a sleek reedbuck, which bounded away down the mountain with graceful abandon, sure-footed and free. Giving up the chase, Vicki stood up on her short hind legs to look over the tops of the grasses. The fragrance of mist came with the downdraft from the mountaintop.

Keeping my secret, I remained in the peace of the mountains. My sister decided it would be safer for me to stay on the farm with her and not attempt to expose myself to the dangers of the outside world. My daughter went to London to specialize, and my son went to a boarding school in Natal that was only a few kilometers from the farm. But newspapermen found their way over the lonely mountain track leading to the farm and the sinister fog of politics spread its fetid breath to the farm boundary. Little did I realize the depths of the covetous lust of men as they planned to kidnap me with the forming child within my womb.

No longer could I take to the road in my MG, speeding with the freedom of a bird. The wings of a vast security net cast its shadow over the fair land of Natal. My every move was checked and set out to a pattern arranged by those in authority. Even if I set out for the mountaintop again—where I longed to go and meditate to tune in to the far reaches of the sky—watching eyes would be everywhere. Cameras with telescopic lenses would be trained on the mountain. I knew this was all for my own safety, and a warm feeling of security and happiness would bring a flush to my cheeks.

One morning I stood on the ridge behind the homestead, beyond the oak wood. As I looked across the rolling grassland to the heights of Cathkin rising steeply in a vast hump in the center of the high Drakensberg range, the words sounded in my mind:

"Back to Cathkin, go back to Cathkin, upon the high plateau."

Akon! It was Akon—and he was telling me to go into hiding.

The great plateau at the foot of Cathkin Peak is a vast nature reserve where the universe has provided the freedom of security to be forever a part of our heritage and where the spaceship of light can still land unmolested and free. The rugged heights will forever retain the secrets of the universe. Its flat-topped peak and rock faces, seamed and seared by the ravages of weather, gaze ever upward into the sky that holds the reality of existence within the freedom of space.

Early the next morning, we saddled the horses and rode away across the Little Mooi river and over the rolling grasslands to Cathkin, away into the mountain fastnesses. The weather was beautiful and the going soft over the veld that rolled for kilometers uplands to the steep grass-mantled slopes at the base of the Drakensberg. Selene covered the distance in her comfortable sure-footed stride with complete ease, tossing her proud head in the fresh wind. She enjoyed the wide-open spaces of the uplands, her ancient Arabian lineage showing in every rippling muscle and the smoothness of her tireless gait.

We slowed the pace a little, as the following pack horse was handicapped by his Shire ancestry and the groom had difficulty in keeping him up with us. We were anxious to keep moving and reach the shelter of the mountains, because the whiteness of Selene could be seen for many kilometers.

We stayed in a remote mountain hostel that nestled at the foot of the high plateau, where Cathkin rises sheer and beautiful from steep, grass-mantled shoulders. Deep gullies and streams were bordered by thick natural bush, where rhododendrons and maidenhair ferns grew in profusion. This country harbored many species of buck and birds. The owls, the hawks and the baboons held sway over the higher slopes and the rock faces that towered above, sheltering the kloofs and valleys below from the dry winds of the interior.

The glory of silence enfolded me with its peace, and the fragrance of damp earth and undergrowth came with the breeze through the waving seed heads of grass. The late summer sun lowered toward the mountain ramparts, deepening the blue of sky. A lovely hush breathed through the vastness of Earth. I lay in the warm grass on the long slope above the hostel, watching the ever-changing mountain. I pondered the wonder and beauty of life, as the Sun lowered still more toward the mighty cliffs and the wind died to a whisper through the grass.

Life is electricity, and how few are born with their awakening consciousness aware of the magic lease we sense as life. To be able to tune in to the infinite consciousness of the soul is to become immortal and join in the realms of dimensions beyond. Thus one attains the spiritual companionship of affinities, and the knowledge of the role they play in shaping our destiny.

THE SUN'S SYSTEM IS OVER FIVE BILLION YEARS OLD AND IS INDEED THE CRADLE OF HUMANKIND.

Humankind must forever seek and find the grandeur in nature to fulfill the longing of the questing soul. To gaze with wonder and awe upon the mighty mountain peaks, forever facing the blue of heaven, is the beginning of the soul's quest to reach the stars in the vast fathoms beyond and tune in with the harmony of the universe. There is wisdom in the harmony of the universe in which we have our being. It is for us to maintain this harmony within our minds and bodies, with all the organs in tune with each other, so that no discord of disease—caused by the discord of the emotions transformed to the heartbeat—may enter. Light, which is electricity, is the universal rhythm to which our bodies are connected in the harmony of music vibrating through the distant reaches of space.

Many are still dormant, their souls not yet awakened to the quest nor aware of the magic force within to seek into the furthermost glories of nature. These are a prelude to the everlasting contact with the intelligent universe, as the soul taps the knowledge and wisdom to transmit it to the mind. Wisdom is born in many who know these things through their enlightened souls. It does not come from the reading of innumerable books and literature, which merely hold the beliefs and ideas of others who have not always spent their time in the quest for truth.

A different kind of people must evolve on Earth. A new species of humans must appear—people of understanding, love and tolerance, who are set on life rather than violence and death, who will become the sons and daughters of their God, the sons and daughters of the universe in harmony with all nature. Only in this way can there be a prelude to the salvation of their world—their Earth, fragile and beautiful, floating alone and vulnerable in the vast void of darkest space, yet shining with a blue light like a beacon of hope.

I thought of all the other planets in our solar system harboring the form of humankind. I thought of how Venus, the mother planet, had given birth to humankind, her beauty unspoiled by the human hand but reduced to desert by the radiation from her star, the Sun. No wonder we feel an affinity with Venus, the mother planet who created so many of us in the dim and distant past. So many people have written of their experiences with Venusian space people in vintage spaceships, and this is indeed so. It is only natural for them to refer to Venusians and Saturnians, because all space people originated from planets in this solar system. The Sun's system is over five billion years old and is indeed the cradle of humankind.

It is simpler for the minds of people on Earth in the present time to expand in the knowledge of their own solar system first. This has been necessary in order to condition them to the greater truths to come. They now have to realize that human beings have lived on Earth before, more than fifty thousand years ago, and as they perfected their science and technology, they were able to move out to a neighboring solar system in the constellation of Centaurus.

This great civilization's people are still referred to as Venusians, however—a tall, fair-skinned people with high foreheads and golden hair. This is Akon's civilization, and I can remember—through race memory— my life on Venus in a previous incarnation. Akon has awakened this memory within my mind and it all comes back with lucid remembrance. Sometime in the future, I shall write a sequel to this book, which I shall call "Daughter of Venus," for indeed, I am a true daughter of Venus and not of Earth.

Perhaps I was planted here as a child, because I do not resemble my family here physically, mentally or spiritually. It is quite natural for me to be a part of Akon's civilization instead of this Earth civilization. Even Akon said to me once, "Why do you refer to May as your sister? She is not a blood sister."

The link of adaptation was between Venus and Earth, and now it is between Meton and Earth, the home planet in the system of Alpha Centauri. In that moment of thinking, my being had contacted the essence of infinity, and the truth was revealed in all its wonder. Time was the essence and the answer to it all—the passage of time was of no consequence to Akon's civilization. Thousands and thousands of years pass unnoticed in the scale of universal knowledge. Earth people need to understand the eons of time, as they do not yet live long enough to mature and attain great wisdom and knowledge. Wisdom and knowledge are born of timelessness, as all events in a solar system are interrelated. The variability of time is of consequence to Akon's civilization. They use it and control it for the benefit of their science. I felt sure that Akon would tell me more about it when next we met.

Quietly I got up out of the long grass and walked down the contour path back to the hostel hidden in the trees. Selene was already bedded down safely in the stable for the night with the other horses, and I arranged with the groom to have them ready at dawn to leave for the high plateau. I warned my son of what we must do, as the darkness of a moonless night closed in around the hostel and we sat out on the terrace looking toward the heights of Cathkin.

The next morning we moved slowly in single file up the steep and winding path. We topped the mountain to the high plateau as the Sun rose over the rolling hills of Natal far below, bathing the grassy slopes of Cathkin with a golden light. Increasing our pace as we reached the plateau, we saw the mighty battlements of Cathkin rising sheer into the clear blue of the morning sky. The rose rock was seamed and scarred from centuries of weathering, forever gazing into the eternity of space, and the lower slopes were alive with a mantle of green grass bowing and waving in the wind.

Suddenly, the mare in front shied off the trail in a frantic effort to escape from the unknown. She almost unseated David, who recovered instantly to control and calm her. Selene snorted, flaring her nostrils, and stopped dead in her tracks. The Zulu groom, riding one horse and leading the great pack horse behind, shouted a command to the horses as he leapt to the ground to try and quiet the terrified animals. But they stood trembling and snorting, showing the whites of their eyes. I immediately jumped from Selene, instructing David to dismount as well, and spoke urgently to the groom in his own tongue to lead the horses some distance away.

Then, across the trail in front of us, Akon's great spaceship shimmered into view. First, a heat-wave effect moved over the flattened grass, and then the glowing ship appeared, hovering low and gradually settling to land on the trail. Further back, the Zulu groom stood rooted to the spot, his mouth opening and shutting. He attempted to shout something to us, but his mind was quite unable to absorb the scientific explanation of the light-bending effects of the unified field. Here was magic indeed at the foot of the rain mountain. All his life he had watched how the clouds gathered to bring the rain to the lands of his people on the rolling hills below. He had seen how the mountain trapped the moisture in the air, creating clouds to bring the rain spreading outward along the vast escarpment and away across the hills to the sea. Now the magic of the mountain had brought something else, something beyond his simple understanding—a spaceship from the wider universe suddenly appeared before his terrified gaze and quietly came to rest upon the trail he knew so well.

Silently, the spaceship remained, and without a sound the doorway opened. Akon stepped through, and with a happy cry of welcome I was gathered up in his arms.

"You Can Never Capture the Spaceship or Its Crew."

How wonderful was that glorious morning spent with Akon! His healing hands smoothed away the seeds of tiredness from my body after the long ride. My fatigue was of short duration, and the sustenance he gave us restored my strength. My life was whole in its unity with Akon, and we had created another life to complete this wholeness. I now relaxed in complete happiness as I sensed the stirring of his child in my womb. It was the first vigorous movement of a strong and healthy son, who seemed to sense already the proximity of his sire as Akon placed his hand on my tummy to feel the beating of his heart.

"You will be safe now, until I fetch you," Akon said softly as he walked with me over to the horses. "You will know when and where to wait for me."

Quieting the horses with his hands and voice, he lifted me into the saddle and stroked Selene's neck.

"She is sure-footed, smooth and comfortable. The rhythmic exercise is good for both of you, and above all, this fresh air up here is full of oxygen. But do not get tired."

With that stern command, he kissed me tenderly and turned back to his spaceship. It seemed that David and the groom did not exist. He took no notice of them. A shimmer like a heat-wave effect played along the ground and shifted up into the sky, and the great spaceship had gone.

I knew Akon had knowledge that others were in the vicinity, others whose covetous minds kept them ever on the move, others who came from elsewhere on this planet to seek and find the spaceship, to probe its method of propulsion by ruthless means. They would have magnetic instruments with them.

The author on horseback.

"Quickly!" I called out. "We must go back into the mountain."

Turning Selene, I put my heels into her sides. Annoyed, she leapt forward tossing her head and sped away, the others following. When we reached the top of the escarpment, I looked back as the mists began to clear, revealing the winding trail our horses had negotiated with little strain or difficulty. The trail wound down, skirting the stream bank, through an easy pass to the high plateau below. On either side, the magnificent cliff faces of Champagne Castle appeared through the thinning clouds. The great flat top of Cathkin reared above the swirling mists like a sentinel, remote and aloof, apart from the main escarpment, with the peak of Mount Memory piercing the moving clouds beyond.

Dismounting, I slipped the bit out of Selene's mouth and fastened the reins to my saddle so that she could drink from the clear stream with comfort and graze the fresh grass on the bank. I then walked along the sloping plateau of the main escarpment and looked over toward the mountainous country of Basutoland. Some time ago, a mountain fire had been sparked off somewhere in the fastnesses of Basutoland by a woman throwing out the hot embers of a cooking fire. It had swept with the west wind over and down the escarpment on the Natal side and through the rich, seeding grass covering the slopes of Cathkin. It was only halted by an old firebreak down the mountainside, leaving the high plateau beyond untouched by the destructive breath of fire. My feet crunched into the burnt grass where the green blades were growing through again, tingeing the vast landscape with an emerald sheen.

The swirling mist moved up over the top of the Drakensberg, driven by the rising east wind. It thinned and was decaying away in the dry air at the top of the escarpment. Suddenly, there was a sound in the wind-driven silence of the sky. Quickly I moved behind a low stunted bush growing in a hollow beside an enormous rock.

With a high-pitched whistle, a dark gray, metallic spacecraft suddenly appeared and made a perfect vertical landing on a jet of orange flame. There was no reflection from the morning sun on the circular fuselage. It remained dull and colorless, like a rock against the green slopes and the blue sky beyond. Camouflaged for sky or ground, it squatted silently on the mountaintop like a bloated spider, waiting—waiting with ominous intent. No wonder Akon had left in such a hurry. He knew they were watching, but could protect me from them. He was also watching from just overhead, completely invisible—this I was sure of, as I sensed his presence.

MASSIVE CUMULUS CLOUDS RESTED ON THE MOUNTAINS. SNOWY WHITE TOPS, LIKE GREAT CAULIFLOWER HEADS CLEARCUT AGAINST THE ICE BLUE OF SKY, TOLD ME OF A CHANGE TO COME.

A circular hatch on the spacecraft popped open without a sound. The lid hinged back like a porthole, or—and I shivered at the thought— like the cleverly hinged lid of a trapdoor spider's lair. Nothing happened. A deep silence hung in the air, and only the wind whispered through the top of the bush. The spacecraft's smooth, rounded simplicity, jointed with large circular rivets, concealed a machine of tremendous efficiency and superior maneuverability. Quite globular, like a sphere, it had sturdily landed on short tripod legs with wide circular bases. I could see small guidance jet nozzles barely protruding around the perimeter, while underneath, the circular rim of the burn exhaust hung between the tripod legs.

A man appeared through the hatch. He quickly slid down the ladder riveted to the fuselage and jumped to the ground. He stood still, raising his arms and running his fingers through his blonde hair. He drew in deep breaths of fresh mountain air, sighing with satisfaction as the invigorating atmosphere restored his tired mind and body. He then turned to look out over the far distances of Natal beyond the rim of the escarpment with thoughts, I knew, of conquest in his heart.

Another man climbed through the hatch, slid down the ladder and lay on the ground, taking in lungfuls of air. Then, closing his eyes, he slumped, spread-eagled out, into a deep sleep. They must have spent a long time in that confined space, I thought—waiting.

Suddenly, the tall cosmonaut whirled round, his hand on his belt, as he saw Selene slowly making her way up the mountain path to look for me. Noting the bridle and saddle on her, he crouched down.

Selene stopped and, lifting her lovely head high, she saw the strange craft and the man crouching beside it. Like a flash of white light, she turned on her hocks and bolted back down the path. The Russian stood up and deliberately took careful aim with a small tubelike weapon.

"Stop!" I called out. "How dare you attempt to kill my horse!"

Startled, he lowered his arm and turned to face me as I walked out from behind the bush. I was so cross that I nearly walked up to him to slap his face, but I spoke instead.

"How dare you frighten Selene and point a death ray at her! Besides, she could have injured herself down that precipitous path. You have no right to land here. This is my country, not yours, and we are peaceful here."

He looked so grim that I thought he would point that small weapon at me and vaporize me from the face of the Earth, but his gray eyes softened as he looked me up and down.

"I did not expect to meet you so soon," he answered, in perfect English with an Oxford accent.

"There is nothing you can do about it," I said. "Capturing me will not help or make any difference. You can never capture the spaceship or its crew."

"Then why are you here now?" he shot back as he clasped my wrist in a grip of iron.

"I am often here. This is my home."

"You came to meet the man from another planet. He is your lover. We wish to meet him also, to ask his help with space exploration."

"He would not agree to meeting any nation on Earth."

"Then you must stay with me until he does agree to talk with us."

"You have already captured me," I quietly replied.

Pulling my wrist free from his grasp, I sat down on a boulder. There was plenty of time. The groom with the pack horse would be here soon. Selene would follow them up. I could then plan to escape, as long as David remained by the lower stream as I had asked him to.

I looked at the tall Russian. He was very handsome, with regular features and blonde hair. He wore very attractive sideburns, which were long, tinged with white and neatly trimmed. He had recently shaved, and I caught the fragrance of a pleasant lotion. He was middle-aged, with kind gray eyes. He would be reasonable and understanding.

"You have been watching for the spaceship for some time with electronic instruments," I said. "You detected it this morning in this area, so you landed hoping to surprise them. Is that not so?"

"That is so."

"You have been ordered to capture the spaceship at all costs, even to attempt to ram it in midair. Your life as a scientist and the life of your engineer would be expendable, just so that your scientists could ground the spaceship and probe her propulsion systems to pick up clues. But," I continued, "you people don't seem to realize that a spaceship of this nature is on automatic control immediately when the propulsion systems are switched on. It takes evasive action the moment a strange object of any kind approaches. Therefore, it is impossible to ram it. What you have been doing is to try and catch it off guard while it is on the ground with all systems switched off. Even then it is impossible to capture her, because a warning device is immediately triggered within the ship. The surrounding field differentials are set up, which nothing can penetrate— not even bullets."

"That would be far too difficult," he answered. "My mission is to capture you."

I bit my lip and said nothing, but shivered suddenly in the warm sun. The Russian looked concerned and immediately climbed into his craft, returning with a thick hand-knitted jersey. Putting it round my shoulders, he buttoned it up, pinning my arms to my side.

"I will take care of you, and when we reach Moscow, you will be specially cared for in the clinic for exobiology research. Your child will be safely delivered by our team of scientists, who will bring up and train the space child as a great scientist. With his sire's brain, he can show us the way to the stars, as naturally he will wish to follow his people."

"You have it all arranged, then," I answered. "And what will become of me, the empty vessel, once you have delivered the space child safely into the hands of your fellow scientists?"

"You will work for us in the department of space research."

"I think you are just guessing about all this."

"Oh, no," the scientist said gently. "We have methods of finding out. We know everything. I never expected to get you, although I had observed you on your white mare at times."

"Then you used her in a clever ruse to capture me."

"Yes. As a scientist and a lover of animals, I would never have harmed her, nor upset you in any way. You are the prize, with the space child developing within your womb."

"And if I escape?"

"Then we will invade your country to get you."

"You wouldn't dare."

"Oh yes, we will. This country is a rich prize that we intend to take."

I turned my back on him and looked out over the rim of the escarpment just as the groom rode over the brow with Selene following on behind. The groom had had enough shocks for one day, and he busied himself with the horses. Selene tossed her head and snorted in defiance as she came to me and thrust her muzzle into the small of my back, pushing me forward off the boulder. I put my arm round her neck, untied the reins and adjusted my stirrups.

I called to the groom to make a fire and brew tea. The Russian's eyes widened as he watched the groom unpack pieces of kindling wood and gather stones to make a fireplace in the sandy hollow beside the great rock. Opening the large saddlebag, he brought out a tin of sandwiches and various items for tea-making. After arranging the mugs on a ledge, he went to fill the billycan from the mountain stream and soon had it boiling in the hot embers.

"My lady, you come with the comforts of civilization," the Russian said, sipping his tea with relish.

"Wouldn't your engineer like some, too?" I replied. "We all share alike. It is a Zulu custom. You had better wake him."

The engineer's pleasant face lit up with a disarming smile, showing prominent, even teeth. His dark hair was so close-cropped that I could see the pale skin of his skull, and he wore casual civilian clothes with

The author mounted on Selene.

black sandshoes on his feet. When he had finished his tea and sandwiches, he climbed back into the craft. I immediately noticed a radar scanner swivel around on top of the craft as it moved into view, and I heard the static of a radio as another antenna appeared under the flange around the periphery of the craft.

Well, I thought, they are all set to go! I twisted my hand in Selene's mane when the Russian said, "Come now, we must go."

At that instant, an Air Force jet screamed across the sky. Noting the look of uneasiness on his face as he suddenly turned to watch the jet, I nodded to the groom and swung up into the saddle from a thick flat stone I had my foot on, driving my heels into Selene's sensitive side. Shocked by my action, she leapt over the bank to slither and slide down the steep trail beyond, with the groom close on our heels. Sliding down on her hocks with the scree, Selene swiftly obeyed me as I guided her in under a wide rock outcrop that overhung the trail further down. The other horses followed, pushing against each other, their sides heaving with the breath of sudden exertion and sweat streaming from their coats as if they already sensed the urgency of our flight.

Except for their labored breathing, they made no sound on the damp sand of the cave floor, and I gave instructions to turn their heads to face the rock wall at the back of the cave. They remained trembling in every limb, sensing some dreadful happening. It came with a strange sound as a great boulder beside the trail outside melted away, as the craft unleashed a deadly high-energy ray from its swivelling turret.

They could not reach any further, as the trail bent sharply to the right and the cave stretched well into the mountainside. All they could do now was to frighten me into submission with their diabolical weapon and this show of horrifying power. I depended on their short margin of time to remain landed on the top of the Berg, for surely they would soon have to rendezvous with their space station. I had noticed the engineer prepare for takeoff and had acted with split-second timing to escape. With perfect timing, the Air Force jet had distracted the Russian's attention. The groom had also helped, being quite wonderful and calm as he unobtrusively prepared for our sudden escape on the top of the Berg.

We remained silently sitting on our mounts for some time, and we only moved from our hideout when thick mist swirled up over the mountain slopes with the south wind—the blessed mist with the fragrance of eternity. Silently and slowly we made our way down the trail to the high plateau. I knew the men in the spacecraft had highly sensitive electronic instruments to pinpoint any area, now that their orbital landings had been perfected to such a degree of accuracy. I thought of the melted sandstone boulder way back up the trail, and I wondered what geologists would think if they found it.

Quickening our pace, we moved across the high plateau and into the shelter of the foothills of Little Berg. Back at the hostel hidden in the pine wood, we rested after our ordeal. Massive cumulus clouds rested on the mountains. Snowy white tops, like great cauliflower heads clearcut against the ice blue of sky, told me of a change to come. Their base showed an ominous depth of blue-black lying like a band across the foothills, gradually settling further and further down as the awe-inspiring cumulonimbus, black and frightening, scudded before a shifting wind. An eerie hush lay in the atmosphere, and all living creatures grew quiet and scurried to shelter. Not a sound or breath of wind stirred in the long grass. All was deadly quiet, until from far away came the distant rumble of thunder.

Selene nudged me in the back with her muzzle and started to paw the ground impatiently. Turning swiftly, I mounted as she turned on her hocks and galloped away toward the stone hut. A thin wisp of smoke curled up in the far distance. Would we reach the hut in time? My thoughts gave wings to Selene, and she lowered her head, stretching out in the fantastic gallop of the Arabian. Her mane and tail streamed in the wind of her passage like a streak of light in the gathering gloom. Burying my hands in her mane, I crouched low over her withers and, moving as one, we jumped over washaways and banks in our swift flight over the veld. The lazily curling smoke gave me the answer. David could read the writing in the sky and had everything ready for a storm siege—even a hot meal cooking on the stove. As we raced toward it, I blessed the stone hut for its shelter and hoped it could withstand the coming onslaught.

Selene checked and pulled up outside the door, her nostrils flaring wide. Quietly, she walked into the hut with me still crouched over her neck. David slammed the stout wooden door just as a bolt of lightning tore a furrow in the ground near the entrance with a whiplash explosion and crack.

Glancing through the window, I saw the light outside change to a blue-green of ominous hue. The veld suddenly ended in a dark line of oblivion. Advancing rapidly and closing in with an awful roar, the pounding hail obliterated everything in its path. I saw the sudden gale tug and claw through the scrub trees beside the mountain stream as great jagged lumps of ice bounced over the veld. They crashed on the corrugated iron roof of the hut, denting the tough iron over our heads with indentations like craters. It sagged inward, but it held firm on the stout roofing timbers.

Darkness enveloped us, and the din was a shocking crescendo of storm havoc. The oil lamp on the trestle table flamed and smoked with each gust of wind that tore at our shelter in its diabolical fury. We stacked the fire with extra wood to give us warmth against the brutal, howling elements without.

Incessant, vicious lightning and the roar of thunder and hail never ceased for a moment. The blinding white of the lightning seared my eyes, flashing through the uncurtained window. I put on my sunglasses as protection from its glaring brilliance, and the dreadful barrage of ice came in through the window, seeking us out as if it had a mind of its own. It pounded through, splintering the wooden frames to bits and smashing against the stone lintel. We found more firewood behind the stove and stacked it in the wide window ledge to block the smashed window. Selene stood with her head down in the corner of the hut, her beautiful white body trembling with nervous tension created by the strong magnetic forces of the storm center. Every now and then she snorted her defiance at the elements. She refused the food and water placed beside her.

We ate some of David's delicious stew, and the warmth of it restored our strength in the fitful glare of lightning. We kept vigil through the night with more hot stew and milk to warm us, and I blessed the builder of the hut for his foresight in constructing such a tough shelter on a knoll well above the stream, which had now added its roar to that of the storm.

Completely exhausted, I curled up in the hay beside Selene. David covered me with a brightly colored Basuto blanket. Gradually, a delicious warmth spread to my feet, and I slept despite the shattering din.

"It Was Wise to Leave the Other Horses in the Shelter of the Hostel. I Felt We Should Not Bring Them."

I awoke to peace and complete quiet. Selene was lying down in the warm hay, her head against my legs, breathing softly in her sleep. David was sitting in front of the dying embers of the fire, his tall body relaxed and serene as he gazed into the fire, keeping vigil for us.

The dawn light brightened through the shattered window and the chinks of wood, and a fresh mountain breeze came through, bringing the pungent smell of bruised vegetation. Taking a deep breath of it, I stretched and then sat up. Selene immediately got to her feet and shook herself, showering bits of veld hay all over me, then put her muzzle deep into the bucket of water, drinking it all down with long gulps.

Selene and friends.

As David opened the door, it was forced back by the tremendous weight of packed hail without. Ice lay banked up against the stone walls. Going to the window, I removed some logs and looked out over a bank of hail packed solid up to the ledge. A cold mist filtered in off the hail, and the slope without was packed with it right down to the stream, which was now a raging torrent bordered with ice. The broken bodies of buck, baboons, hares, snakes and rats and birds of all kinds, mixed with lumps of hail, swept past with the current. Some remained in an eddy beside the bank—broken, lifeless bodies battered to death by the vicious storm and swept into the merciless flood. What a terrible toll—and we would have been added to the massacre, but for the shelter of the stout hut.

I pondered for a moment the ruthless way of nature and said, "You know, Dave, we are no more important than a blade of grass in the infinity of the universe."

After a good breakfast, we waited for the rising sun to melt the hail. Selene put her head down and sniffed the hail, snorting and pawing at it. I could see she was longing to gallop free over the veld as is the way of horses in the exhilarating wind after a storm. She checked herself, however, sensing the slippery danger on the ground and the devastation of the storm's aftermath. Instead, she stood still and we gave her some lucerne to eat.

"It was wise to leave the other horses in the shelter of the hostel," I said. "I felt we should not bring them."

"Yes, I'm glad I walked up. How did you know, Mom?"

"By observing the clouds early yesterday morning as we were preparing to ride up here to meet Akon."

Great drifts of hail lay about, and we had difficulty in negotiating the path down the slopes on our way back to the hostel, as it was choked with ice and debris. Before I went into a deep sleep, I could hear the soothing sound of the nearby waterfall as it tumbled over the krans into the depths of the pool below. Its gentle rushing brought me slowly awake in the morning.

We were soon off again, winding our way up the path over the foothills to the high plateau and away to the foot of Cathkin. The atmosphere was crystal clear and the great mass of Cathkin soared into the blue sky in perfect detail. Every crevice and shelf was clear and sparkling in the sunshine. The sheer rock faces were cleansed and beautiful, as nature recovered with rapid vitality everywhere after the savage onslaught of the devastating hailstorm.

The going was soft for the horses, and we moved swiftly across the high plateau. A troop of baboons paused in their rummaging for beetles and roots in the soft rain-soaked earth to watch our passage. They were the lucky ones, I thought, whose wise leader had taken them all into the shelter of a cave before that vicious cloud let loose its barrage of ice. The baboon leader gave us a deep bark of recognition and then resumed his search for succulent creatures under rocks and tufts of veld grass.

We rode on to the foot of Cathkin Peak itself, where the steep, grass-mantled slopes folded into the streambed. There, we dismounted in the shade of indigenous trees sheltered in the folds of the steep slopes and made camp to await the coming of Akon.

The horses quietly drank the clear sparkling water and grazed about the banks, contentedly pushing each other out of the way with their muzzles, while we made tea with honey to sweeten it and ate whole-wheat sandwiches with lettuce and tomatoes. The only sound was the gentle rushing of the stream and the sigh of the breeze through the trees. Another day and another night passed before Akon landed in his spaceship of light, and we were together again in the safe and remote fastness of Cathkin.

"My beloved, it is safe for you to return to the farm," Akon said to me one evening as we sat on the grassy bank beside the rushing mountain stream. "Go back and rest, and I shall fetch you from there."

So we spent another few wonderful days with Akon in the fastness of the mountains, before taking the horses quietly back to the farm.

CHAPTER 6

BEYOND THE TIME BARRIER: TO ALPHA CENTAURI

There was consternation back on the farm. Cookie, my sister's little white dog—a special pet of the family—was missing.

"We've called and called," my sister, flushed and wretched, told me. "We cannot find him."

"Oh . . ."

I could say no more, because I knew in my heart what had happened. The poor little creature, I thought, and my throat tightened as I visualized the scene of his demise. Being white, he was looked upon as the white woman's familiar spirit. His value as something unusual was enhanced since he had been seen watching, without fear, the great ship from the universe. Being white and male, he was indeed strong *umuthi*[1], and powerful *umuthi* would have to be found because a white man had landed in his magic wagon on the mountaintop.

My sister was too miserable to wonder at all. She had tried everything and offered a substantial reward to recover Cookie. All the farm women, children and men had turned out to search, aided by two trained hunters with their dogs. They found only silence—a sinister silence, and nothing else.

"I'm a bit worried," Jock said thoughtfully, "about the groom and that wife of his. Since those ritual murders on the border, she has been forcing him along a very slippery path."

---

1. *medicine*

"That means . . ." I whispered. I left the statement unfinished, though, as I suddenly realized that Muti was waiting. He must know something, I thought.

"*Inkosazana*, last night I went to my *n'yanga*[1] just over the river here to ask of the dog. He is dead. M'Kay brought a bitch in season to the garden. When your little white dog came out, M'Kay caught him and took him away. That night he died. He was sacrificed—a ritual murder, as you call it—because a white creature at mating time is very good medicine. For a piece of his liver no bigger than your little fingernail, people will pay much money. Such *umuthi* makes them strong and able to procreate and add children to their wealth. Sexual weakness is regarded with abhorrence. This medicine also keeps evil spirits away.

"But the little dog's eyes were especially valuable, as no other creature's would be, because he had sat in the grass and watched the great cloud ship without fear. Because of this, he will give the strength of that white man from the clouds to those who consume his liver."

"Be quiet about this," Jock told Muti. "The *N'kosigaas* will say nothing until we have found, through the police, our own *n'yanga* to tell us. The sergeant suggested we ask for the truth through the Zulu system—there is a woman he recommended."

"FEAR NOT. AKON WILL COME FOR ME."

The next day, they interviewed a woman named Bolofet. She was fey, and trusted by the police as fearless and truthful. She was known throughout the country. In her beehive-shaped hut, made of tambooti grass tied to a shell of slender wattle saplings, the white people sat on chairs while she sat on her heels on a grass mat facing the light. A girl grandchild came and lay against her hip. My sister gave her the requested fee and the little white dog's small tartan coat. Bolofet told the same tale Muti had heard. She added that the dog had been moved the afternoon before from the loose earth on the dam wall, and his body thrown into the swift, snow-fed river with a stone tied to it.

"No evidence left now with the body gone," muttered Jock.

"Thank you, Bolofet," my sister said. "Who did this?"

---

1. *witch doctor*

"M'Kay," replied the woman.

"So it was my trusted groom," my sister said thoughtfully. "Poor little Cookie. He was never really happy or comfortable after he went blind watching the spaceship. Remember, the vet said he probably got frightful headaches. Perhaps that pagan-hearted M'Kay will get headaches too. I wonder how he knew Cookie couldn't see at all—I wonder if he did know?"

"He simply used him to absorb Akon's strength and greatness," I answered.

"Then we must protect you, my dear, because once they know Akon has made you pregnant . . . "

My sister suddenly realized the terrible implications, and her face blanched with anxiety.

"Then there are the politicians," she went on. "They will try and get you, and the terrorists will attempt to kidnap you. What are we going to do? I shall appeal to the authorities again for protection."

"Then again," she said, placing her hand to her heart, "the mark of lineage will be seen in the facial features of the developing life within you, once he is born."

"Fear not," I said softly, feeling the joy of the quickening body within mine. "Akon will come for me. His son will not be born on this planet, where a racialistic outlook submerges all sane and intellectual thought. His skin is also white, of a golden hue, born of a fair-skinned race, and as you rightly say, this mark of lineage will be seen in his facial features."

An exhilarating happiness filled those days of quickening life within me. The halcyon days were filled with joy—with a life so precious, a part of Akon to be nurtured, protected and loved, a life from another planet to be encompassed with the essence of love and joy that a woman knows and gives to the quickening child within her womb when the embryo stems from the seed of love. This is the spark that creates the divine soul in human life, a divine soul born in the offspring of a true mating between a man and a woman. True and complete love, of a man for a woman and a woman for a man, is so rarely found among human beings on Earth, who misunderstand the functions of mating and procreation in the higher octaves of sensual delight.

One golden day I sensed the nearness of Akon. My heart became restless as I awaited a sign in the evening sky. The full moon rose over the line of hills in the east, and the still and tranquil hush of evening light spread over the darkening mountains to the west. I kissed May goodbye.

"I know you will care for David," I said. "Bless you!"

And I was gone in the MG, winding along the mountain track to the top of the hill behind the homestead beyond the oak wood.

I had not long to wait. The beautiful ship of light appeared, moving silently through the moonlit atmosphere. Opalescent and ethereal in the moonbeams, it quietly settled on the hilltop. Bluish, unearthly light streamed from the portholes, and the ship remained silent for a few brief moments. The automatic doors opened then, and Akon stepped through. He came to me and picked me up in his arms, holding me close.

"Now I am really going to carry you off with me to another planet," he whispered, his lips in my hair as he carried me into the spaceship.

Sheron smiled a greeting from his control desk, and Haben was there too.

"Hello my dear," he said, as Akon put me on my feet. "You look beautiful and well—and also large with child as we hoped. It suits you. There is a radiance about you. The child is due to be born."

"When a child is born, we must reach for the stars," Akon said. "We have just moved from Mars, and must now be off again to Alpha Centauri."

"But my car! I cannot just leave her out there on the hill."

"We will take the car too," said Akon. "We never had piston engines like that, and besides, the engine needs some adjustment. I shall attend to that myself."

"Can You Visualize It All Now in Your Mind?"

Sheron pressed a lever beside the control panel, and I saw a ramp slide out from an opening in the hull. A brilliant beam of white light enveloped the MG. It rose, suspended within the light, and was drawn swiftly forward onto the ramp and into the hull of the spaceship. The ramp instantly slid back, leaving no trace of an opening in the side of the hull.

"The MG is quite safe in the hold, my beloved one," Akon smiled. "You won't need it on the home planet—there are no filling stations there and no roads. Such an antiquated mode of transport would appear out of place."

Sheron adjusted the pushbuttons on the control panel. I sensed again that fantastic vibration, like a shudder from outside the sealed cabins, as the spaceship moved in instantaneous anti-light harmonics, stepping up the frequency interaction of the speed of light and speeding up the geometric of time, altering the frequencies controlling the matter-antimatter cycles—the geometric matrix of space-time.

I closed my eyes and relaxed on the comfortable bench as Akon placed his hand on my forehead. I felt a harmonic affinity with all substance, a resonance tuned to matter and antimatter in alternate pulses.

"You understand now, my beloved, the nature of our propulsion systems. The equation is quite clear within your mind. You can move in harmony with us. You can know the beautiful simplicity of nature as we alter the micro-atoms of light, the basic building blocks of all energy and matter—pure electromagnetic waveforms, the key to the universe and all life, where all protons and neutrons are built up from micro-atoms. Can you visualize it all now in your mind?"

"Yes, indeed!" I replied. "I can see it all so clearly in all its glorious simplicity—assemblies of micro-atoms throughout all matter and anti-matter, consisting of three within four in alternate pulses. The whole universe is a pulse of energy, resonating in harmonic interaction to form different waveforms.

"Physical matter, like this spaceship and ourselves, is nothing more than a concentrated field of force. We are made up of these waveforms, and we can feel and see similar waveforms that resonate within our range of frequencies. The spaceship achieves a shift in space-time simply by stepping up the frequencies of light and time between each pulse of physical matter. It is a planet formed by three spiraling wave motions in space, and it repositions itself within the spatial dimensions of the planet by decreasing frequencies between pulses. Thus it appears in the time geometric of the planet, which can be anywhere in space—in the Sun's system or in another solar system altogether.

"Created by the harmonic interaction of the unified field differentials emanating from the spaceship herself in terms of light, or pure electromagnetic waveform, the unified field equation manifests in perfect harmony. I can see now the simple equation that creates it all. The letters and the figures are clearly seen in my mind—there is no need to write the formula down. The mathematical precision and placing of the numbers and letters will remain forever within my mind. It is already within the mind of our child, who will now be born with this knowledge of highly advanced physics."

"Good. This is how it must be. You are an excellent pupil, my dear, and indeed worthy to be one of us and the mother of my son."

Akon held me close in his arms, pressing my head against his chest with his left hand so that I could feel the strong beat of his heart in rhythmic perfection.

And Then I Saw It—Another Brilliant Sphere, another Home of Life, another Island Moving in the Vast Void of Space, another Venus.

"There are two of you to look after now. My child within you is stirring and will be born as soon as we reach my home. Your bloodstream has been cleansed by the pure, fresh air in the spaceship. Despite your living for many months on the farm where the air was clean, the amount of pollution in Earth's atmosphere now encircles the entire planet. It has reached a very dangerous level. Because of this measure of pollution, we only land on the high remote areas of mountains. Come. There is a bath and change of garments for you in the small cabin." Holding me close and whispering words of love, he went with me into the smaller cabin.

The single garment I put on hung in rich and soft folds of silk to my ankles. Simple and free, it concealed the thickening of my waist, hanging from the shoulders. It had wide, loose sleeves like a caftan and shimmered golden yellow with threads of green.

"The golden silk matches your amber eyes," Akon said softly. He cradled my feet in his big hands. "Your feet are small and broad—there is no need for the restriction of shoes."

He fitted a beautiful pair of silken sandals, the color of the sapphire sea, to my feet. Then he changed out of his silvery suit into a garment of soft glowing silk and a pair of sandals like mine.

Haben called to us to come and watch the viewing lens. We moved toward the shining, curved wall, our thoughts triggering the electronic doorway that slid open at our approach.

I caught my breath with excitement as I glimpsed tremendous colors in the lens. The most awe-inspiring spectacle was taking shape, suffused in brilliant yellows, rose red and blue with vast streamers of soft rose red that reached out into the silken darkness of fathomless space. The brilliant colors cleared after a moment, and two gigantic stars glowed in the far reaches of the void. One shone with deep blue radiation, and the other with a glory of rose red. A third, much smaller, star vibrated in soft golden light radiation in a wide orbit around the two.

This was Alpha Centauri, seen in all the glory of pristine radiation. The great, waxing stars balanced each other in the prime of their lifespans, harboring a race of people who tame the winds of space to propel their beautiful spaceships. Through the filtered lens, I watched stupendous prominences looping out and shifting in continuous agitation as rhythmic waves and branches of light emitted outward from the photosphere in dense radiation. Stupendous energy filled the vast reaches of space that surrounded the splendor of this triple solar system, and the glory of Akon's home system filled the lens with magnificent color and movements.

And then I saw her—another brilliant sphere, another home of life, another island moving in the vast void of space, another Venus. This was Meton, or Venus II—the home of an advanced race of people, a world of gentle climate and gentle people, vast seas of sapphire blue and emerald isles in an atmosphere similar to Venus when it had lived, harboring the beginnings of this fantastic race of people.

Other planets could be seen with their bright atmospheres, moving with a slow and graceful purposefulness around the small golden star. The star moved with its retinue of seven planets in orbit about the two great stars, well within the tremendous corona of this magnificent star system known to Earth people as Alpha Centauri.

"The star of our system is known to Earth people as Proxima Centauri, and all these planets are inhabited by our civilization. We live in constructive harmony and peace. We moved from Venus in the Sun's system to make our home here, which is now permanent because we can control our environment. Our science and our understanding of stars, planets and solar systems have advanced considerably since we lived on Venus. Venus, to us, is still the home planet—the cradle of our race—and it is for this reason that we come into the Sun's system to touch down on that planet's surface and bring it to life again. Beneath her desert surface she still lives and thrives. The beautiful mountains of rose-colored rocks will again breathe an atmosphere of cerulean sky, and the moisture-giving clouds will spread out over the surface to form the seas again."

"And the variable star of her system, the Sun . . . can you now tame the Sun?" I asked

"Indeed, yes. This is what we are in the process of doing."

"Will it change the climate on Earth?"

"Of course. All planetary weather is controlled by the star of the planet's solar system."

"And a triple system like this one?"

"These are stable, waxing stars without magnetic anomalies," Akon explained. "They interact with harmonic resonance, creating equable climates over the planets. This also makes it much safer for our spaceships to operate in harmonic interaction with the unified field of matter and antimatter. Anomalies in Earth's atmosphere have caused fatal accidents to two of our spaceships when the matter-antimatter cycle of their propulsion systems shifted frequencies while moving within the resonating fields of the system. Tremendous explosions resulted, releasing a high level of radiation. Our scientists, at the instant of alarm detection within the spaceships, set course over remote, unpopulated areas of the planet Earth. The explosions occurred in the atmosphere, and unusually high levels of radioactivity remained on the surface."

"Oh. So that clears up the mystery of the Tungus Taiga," I whispered with awe, "where an explosion overhead ripped the forest to bits. And of course, the crew simply disappeared." I could say no more and moved closer to Akon.

The splendor in space of the great stars and the glory of Akon's home system filled the lens like the electric mirage I had seen long ago in the vintage mothership, who could bring this fantastic scene to her people far away in other and strange solar systems, to keep in touch with their time system through the far reaches of interstellar space. The Venusian mothership still retained the highly civilized contact with her people that she had in days of yore, no matter where in the galaxy they had now migrated to.

Moving smoothly within her environment as a natural celestial object, our spaceship appeared high in the atmosphere of the speeding planet Meton—or Venus II—the second planet outward from the golden star, Proxima Centauri. As we descended, a great glistening cloud billowed up over the sea, a curtain of rain trailing and thickening at its base. The radiation from the three stars struck a golden radiance out of the huge cumulus heads that spread out across the sapphire seas.

We approached the circular roof of a home made of glistening material like marble. The beautiful building was set on a dais of surrounding circular steps—perfectly symmetrical, rising from emerald lawns of shining grass and scattered semicircular beds of brilliant flowers. Trees with bright green foliage were scattered across the landscape like a great park.

The spaceship silently settled to the rooftop, its shining surface untarnished by the vast distances it had traveled or the atmosphere of planets. The ship moved beyond the velocity of light, as Earth people understand it, and in so doing it overcame the power of the universe. It annihilated the fathomless seas of space in its swift passage through time, going with the pressure force of the universe—gravity—and attaining the higher octaves of resonance by the absorption of light itself. Thus it annihilated the light barrier.

How afraid Earth scientists were when they attempted to annihilate the sound barrier in the atmosphere with aircraft, I thought. And yet it had all proved to be so very simple—no trouble at all—as it is now with the light barrier. To reach another solar system within seconds, almost instantaneously, proved the simplicity of faster-than-light spaceships or flying saucers.

"I remember in years past how afraid they were of the sound barrier. They didn't know what to expect or how to overcome the problem of speed through the atmosphere of Earth. Geoffrey de Havilland's DH Swallow exploded in an attempt to break the sound barrier, just as some of these beautiful spaceships have exploded while breaking the light barrier."

Sheron pressed a button on the control panel to nullify the spaceship's systems. We waited a few seconds while the field differentials dissipated, and Akon walked toward the shining wall. The door slid open at his thought. I heard joyful voices and laughter as Akon's family came into the spaceship to greet us. Akon took my hand and led me down a single flight of stairs that descended into the home from the landing ramp. A circular balcony of delicately carved railings glowed with the luster of pearl against golden walls. It curved around the building, bringing us to

AKON'S HOUSE ON METON

This is a computer-drafted copy of the author's original drawing.

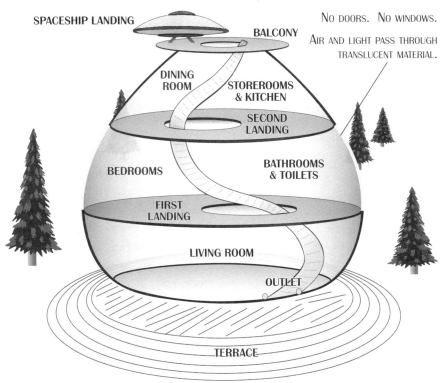

SPACESHIP LANDING

BALCONY

No doors. No windows.

Air and light pass through translucent material.

DINING ROOM

STOREROOMS & KITCHEN

SECOND LANDING

BEDROOMS

BATHROOMS & TOILETS

FIRST LANDING

LIVING ROOM

OUTLET

TERRACE

Trees, grass and flowers, vast lawns.

Light emanates from spiral staircase; thereby, one floats or is drawn in a state of weightlessness.

Staircase slopes gradually, suspended without supports.

Gravity belt used instead of ascending if necessary (of course, I used the stairs).

---

the second floor. I could see the great living room far below—a vast circular chamber full of the glorious colors of the spectrum on the floor, the walls, the couches and the divans.

The spiral staircase curved down the center of the circular building, the banisters hand carved into a lovely delicate tracery of flowers and vines. These carvings were made of the same glowing material I had seen in the spaceship. Putting my hand on the smooth and lovely surface, we slowly walked down.

"But this is pearl!" I said. "Real pearl! It's uneven in places too, and it has that natural pink luster. It's alive and giving out light!"

We paused to admire the lovely carving.

"Our aqueous atmosphere here and in the spaceships keeps pearl alive and vibrant as in its natural habitat, the sea," Akon explained. "We use pearl for the building of our homes and for the construction of our spaceships. Pearl lives on with vibrant light, and we farm this beautiful living substance within our vast seas. We live with it always, as it generates the light of the universe for our energy needs."

"How beautiful to live with! I have always loved pearls."

I looked up into Akon's eyes. He put his arm about my waist so that I could lean against him and take the weight off my feet.

"My beloved, I shall give you pearls to wear always, close to your skin."

He opened a casket attached to the banister and lifted out the most beautiful pearl necklace I had ever seen—two rows of glowing, evenly-matched pink pearls, with a clasp of eight seed pearls surrounding a lovely ruby. I stood spellbound in the center of the stairway as he placed them around my neck. The soft, smooth coolness of the stones caused me to gasp with pleasure, and I put my hand up to press them against my throat.

"Their light will give you light always. Wear them always with the ring, and our communication will remain unbroken forever." Akon put his hand under my chin, lifting my face up to his. "My chosen one, these pearls were left in the casket by my mother. She left them for my chosen one, whom she knew would come from another planet."

MEN OF EARTH LIVE IN A WORLD OF CHAOS AND DESTRUCTION. THESE ARE THE HEIGHTS OF THEIR UNDERSTANDING, AND HYDROGEN BOMBS ARE THE LIMIT OF THEIR POWER.

Pleia and Haben came to me and put their arms about me, hugging and kissing me on both cheeks.

"Welcome home, dear one," said Pleia. "We are your family—your kin."

Theton came forward as well, with his mate Lyra and their three children, to welcome me with a hug and a kiss on both cheeks.

"How wonderful and lovely you all are," I said, my heart brimming over with love for them all. I hugged and kissed each one of them again. "Thank you for letting me come. How happy I am to be here."

I turned to Akon, who gathered me up in his arms and carried me down the stairway, the others following us into the great circular living room. Its beauty took my breath away. Akon stood in the room's center, still holding me in his arms, and I looked up at the perfection of the domed ceiling, painted with the three stars of Alpha Centauri. They shed their life-giving rays throughout the home in a natural lighting emanating from the glowing luminous substance of pearl. I absorbed the beauty of the atmosphere within the home—the color vibrations were particularly strong, with no pale or insipid colors. Everywhere, the bright and glorious colors of the spectrum of nature blended with a deep silky softness that took my breath away.

Delicate music played upon strings wafted through the room from the sound board of the dome above—music of such purity and perfection of composition that its magic thrilled my soul, and my body responded with ecstasy to the vibrations. Gently, Akon set me down, and my silken sandals sank a little into the firm, soft carpeting.

"Music is a universal language," he said. "We feel the vibrations, the harmony of composition. Glorious colors also give out vibrations for our well-being. Plants, as you see them growing in this room, thrive with love, harmony and the vibrations of our music. We live with beauty and comfort."

The homes of the people of Meton were not more than three stories high, I learned, but they only lived in the first two floors. The top story was used for the kitchen and storerooms. They preferred to live and sleep close to the ground—it was healthier to do so, and it allowed them to retain the magnetic impulses emanating from the planet. Those impulses were conducted by the circular construction of the homes themselves, and were released within by the molded pearl.

Meton's people had no tensions or aggressive thoughts, which allowed them to retain their health and longevity. Because of the advanced conditions for living and their way of life, they had no need for a monetary system. The beauty and comforts of life were shared by all inhabitants, resulting in time for the cultivation of the mind and the attainment of a great cultural foundation and background. All knowledge was channelled into constructive work and recreation—the arts and sciences were pursued by all, and produced a greatly advanced and constructive civilization where violence and wars were completely unknown.

"Come, my dear," Akon said. We sat down on a low and very comfortable couch whose high back supported my spine and shoulders. Akon lifted my feet and placed them to rest on a soft, high cushion.

"We maintain harmonious contact with other races on other planets," he continued, "but close contact or miscegenation is unknown among our race beyond this solar system. This is why only a few from beyond this solar system are chosen for breeding purposes, to infuse new blood into our ancient race. We only select those few whom we know to be reborn from the mother planet, Venus. You, my beloved, have this race memory. Your ancient lineage goes back many thousands of years in Earth time. We have traced your ancestry, and all this was arranged when you were born."

"You know so much!" I said, my mind full of wonder. "Even to the birth of your son. You knew it would not be a daughter. How did you know?"

"I took you at the right time," Akon said, "when I detected your vibrations. This had to be done twice. Making love to you twice was the most beautiful experience, and it was also necessary, because having a boy is a lot more difficult! Male-bearing sperm lasts only a few hours, so I had to be accurate within hours about your time of ovulation."

"It was the most beautiful experience of all my life," I whispered as I kissed Akon.

Pleia came into the room bearing a silver tray of refreshments. She brought me a bowl of fruit juice.

"Drink it all down," she said. "It has been out in the light of the stars, absorbing the life-giving radiation that filters through our thick atmosphere. I am so happy you and Akon have mated so perfectly—it rarely happens with other planetary beings. Your son will indeed be very special and unusual. Such mating is very important after all these eons of time, as our race has become very inbred despite our methods of scientific breeding.

"Love will be your bond forever, and your soul belongs here now, although your body still belongs to Earth. When your body dies on Earth, the soul will return here. Your physical body is merely a shell around you to protect the soul of energy. When it falls away, the real you—the divine spark of life—moves on into infinite timelessness in the cycle of evolution."

Pleia kissed me tenderly, and then continued. "The cycle changes again and you become mass again, born into a physical body as you are at present. This process is the cycle of evolution in the soul and mind, and the race memory is retained always within your subconscious. Gradually, you evolve through all the dimensions of time and into eternity, when the body's cells cease to degenerate. Humankind is a part of eternity. We found this great truth when we moved into the far reaches of space beyond the light barrier.

"We all have eternal life in time, the ever-moving present. Only when balance is achieved do we change vibrations, and then we do indeed find the joy in life forever. I can see in the spectrum of time, my dear, that your soul's transient hold on Earth will soon be broken, and you will join us again here forever. It will not be a long wait. Whereas on Earth, one's heartbeat remains attuned to the lower vibrations of time and a slower pulse rate is recorded, here on Meton the heartbeat becomes attuned to the higher vibratory rate in time. The timing of your heartbeats will go out of rhythm in an attempt to keep time with the vibratory rate of this planet's time continuum.

"The herbal juices I have just given you will regulate your heartbeat and prevent any distress. It will allay the effect of our atmosphere on your heart until we have delivered you of Akon's son, so that he may be born on this planet and become attuned to the environment where he belongs." With a flourish of her hand, Pleia concluded by saying, "You know and are happy that he may never breathe the harsh atmosphere now imposed by humankind's pollution of Earth's environment."

Looking through the long open doors of the living room, I saw the deep sapphire blue of the sea. The waters sparkled in gentle waves that washed onto the white beach, the pulse of their energy propagated by the oscillations of water molecules that moved in rhythmic swells from the far horizon. It was a gentle climate, reflected in tranquil seas.

A race is affected by the climate in which it lives. Not here on this planet could the ruthless and prodigious march of storms across land and sea occur, leaving swathes of destruction, chaos, nervous tension and cha-otic changes in magnetic frequency. Spawned by the high winds of an unstable atmospheric pressure, the mighty storms of Earth rule its skies, and people of that planet bow in awe and fright before the onslaught of hostile clouds. Yet these living cells that multiply in the frigid heights—depending on noise and destruction for their progressive march across the face of a planet—can be tamed. Bereft of their destructive power, they can become gentle, and provide the soft rains so necessary for the life of a planet.

People of Earth live in a world of chaos and destruction. These are the height of their understanding, and hydrogen bombs are the limit of their power. The unstable conditions existing there cause low-pressure waves to trigger off faults within the crust of the planet, and the resulting devastation from earthquakes and the heaving seas is a clear indication of the extent to which the Earth's surface breathes the sky.

"I Can Control the Electrical Rhythm of Your Heart for a Limited Period, Which Will Amount to Four Months of Your Earth Time."

On Meton, the balanced radiation of her primary star mingle with the tremendously beneficial radiation from the great binary stars. This planet is enfolded within the enormous corona of her triple system, and the collisions of radiation from the three balanced sources creates a far deeper ionosphere surrounding the planet. This shield is formed when a planet is within the temperature range of stars, which is necessary to create these conditions. Magnetic seas encircle a planet and protect the lower atmospheric envelope, and life as we know it exists on the land, in the air and in the waters.

In the higher atmosphere, beautiful clouds shimmer and shine. The lower nacreous clouds, composed of ice crystals, shine with a mother-of-pearl iridescence. The higher noctilucent clouds, composed of cosmic dust, shine and reflect a silvery white radiance. From space, Meton looks very bright from the reflection of star radiation from these high clouds. It looks much like Venus does from space in Earth's system.

The peace and silence of the atmosphere blew into the room, bringing the fragrance of the land and the tang of the sea, and I longed to go out into the clear, fresh day.

"Come," said Akon, taking my hand. "We shall go to the hilltop. Refreshment for the soul is vital for you, my dear."

We walked quietly through the lush green grass of the hillside to the gently rounded top, and sat down in the fragrant grass and flowers beneath a lovely tree. It was a tree of vast height, reaching straight and tall into the deep blue of the sky. Its graceful branches bore shiny, dark green leaves and swept out in a symmetry of curved strength from the rose-red bark of the trunk.

A gentle breeze from across the sapphire sea fanned my cheeks. With it came the elusive and exotic fragrance of this sea that I had known in the spaceship, as well as many years before on Earth when it came to me as I lay near death in Groote Schuur Hospital in faraway Cape Town—the fragrance that had revived me, giving to me the breath of life again as this glorious scene unfolded about me. Here it was in all its lovely reality, giving me a new lease on life to fulfill my destiny here.

"How long will I be allowed to remain here with you on this lovely planet? Will it be possible to stay even a little while? I feel reborn and rejuvenated, as if my life is now really just beginning." I threw my head back and looked up into the eternal depths of sapphire blue as the fragrant breeze swept up the slope from far across the sea.

"My beloved, I want you to remain with me forever, but this is not possible at present. Your physical body will be unable to acclimate to the higher vibratory rate within our atmosphere that the radiation from our three stars causes. These will affect the rhythm of your heart. Your heart has an electrical timing device that is attuned to the star of your system, the Sun, as we here on this planet are attuned to the frequency of our stars' resonating vibrations. I can control the electrical rhythm of your heart for a limited period, which will amount to four months of your Earth time.

"I intend to keep you with me for this period not only for my sake, but for the sake of our son, who will need his mother's close presence—and for your sake too. You will need the close presence of your child and your mate. This is natural and necessary in life. The absence of this creates psychological trouble and illness that has a lasting effect on children, hence all the throat and tonsil illnesses of children on Earth—they are breathing a polluted atmosphere and are left alone far too much by their parents, which results in fear and lack of security, as well as nervous tension and insufficient sleep and rest. So the body gets out of rhythm, and illness results from the lack of love, constant close proximity, harmony and quiet. The people of Earth are poisoned and sick as a result of their way of life."

"My beloved, how simply wonderful!" I said with joy as I hugged and kissed Akon. "Now I can really live and enjoy every moment of my life here. It's going to be the most wonderful four months of my life. It will give me the strength to carry out my destiny in the future, and to go back to Earth with hope and love for all things in my heart."

"Your heart, though, dearest, will never recover. It will always go out of rhythm now, even back on Earth, where the solar wind or flares will affect it badly at peak periods of the sunspot cycles."

"Oh! But how worthwhile it all is!" I cried to the wide open skies as I flung my arms wide to the universe. "To love you and have your son, and to live with you for four months! Any sacrifice is worth all this. Yet it is no such thing as a sacrifice," I continued, filled with awe and wonder. "That only applies to human ideas. This is life, real life—and my life! Oh, how happy I am! Nothing and nobody can ever take all this away from me. It is my life and will live with me forever, to give me strength and a reason for being—why I am I—so that I could experience all this wonder and beauty, and to give me a reason for living at this cycle in time. It was all meant to be, and nothing can change this. It is the inexorable law of the universe."

"And the universe will take care of you, my dear," Akon said, gently putting his arms about me to lift me from the emerald sward. "As you think and live, so the universe will respond."

"HUMANKIND CAN LIVE AS LONG AS HIS BRAIN CELLS ARE REGENERATED BY THE TRUE BALANCE OF THE LIFE-GIVING RADIATION FROM THE CENTER OF ALL LIFE."

The beautiful, tumbling country rolled on up to great mountains topped with glowing rose-red rock faces, the grassy slopes dotted with golden trees. Clear, sparkling rivers glistened in the star-drenched atmosphere, cascading their way to the sea. Exotic flowers in brilliant colors grew everywhere, and masses of lilies flowered like a carpet in the woods, where nature rules in an abundance of luxuriant flora.

Fish and mammals abound in the seas, lakes and rivers on Meton. There are no large flesh-eating creatures such as sharks, nor are there carnivorous creatures on the land. The land creatures are herbivorous and live on the lush green vegetation. Overstocking is solved by removing surplus creatures to other planets, where similar conditions prevail, so that no destruction of life occurs.

The cattle are a select few, scientifically bred for milk. They have no horns at all and are pure white. Very gentle and friendly, with large soft eyes, they love to lie in the waters of the lakes. There is always a clean, fresh smell about them, and they are never herded into buildings of any kind. They are milked out in the open fields—they come when they are called. Their milk is high in protein and essential minerals, and it has a delicious flavor.

White horses pranced and gamboled over the emerald grasslands, full of fire and spirit but gentle and loving. Trained to respond to thought, they came trotting up to us and gently nuzzled for tidbits. I caught my breath at their beauty. Here were the true equines, the fabled creatures of the heavens that drew the golden chariot of Helios across the aura of the stars. It was they who spawned the Arabians, with their delicate heads and breadth of brow between large gentle eyes, the classic curve lending grace to breadth of nostrils, and with rounded pure white bodies shaped in perfection of bone. Bred in the cradle winds of heaven, the mark of their lineage is cast in a gentler mold. They are like their human friends, who also spawned a race of people on Earth and whose mark of lineage is also cast in a gentler mold, capturing the texture of the clouds from heaven's purity. Fascinated, I watched their graceful movements on the slope of the hill as they cantered down to the stream below.

The birds were the most beautiful I had ever seen. Brilliantly colored, they abounded throughout the lovely land, singing the magic carols of birdsong in the higher octaves of sound. Perfectly tame, they flew down from the skies or the trees to settle with a flutter of importance on your outstretched hand or shoulders. With an abundance of natural food and water, they came for love and affection as they had been encouraged to do by this civilization down through the centuries. They regarded me with friendly unwinking eyes, heads cocked to one side, and burst into trills of enchanting song, liquid and clear, accepting me as a part of the scene as they fluttered and hopped over the grass.

Sighing with relaxed contentment, I lay back on the thick couch of soft grass. Great golden bees hummed and droned among the flowers, and they lulled me to sleep. Akon let me sleep on and on, and he was still sitting beside me when I awakened. Looking up through the branches to the deep blue beyond, I watched a silver ship move across the sky.

"How beautiful!" I murmured. "Real peace, with the soothing rhythm of nature."

Akon smoothed my hair back as he leaned onto his elbow with his face close to mine.

"Our way of life is very simple—a serene and direct approach to all things in life. Truth cannot be hidden, and there is no subterfuge in our attitude of mind. We have no politics, and thus there is peace and harmony in all things controlled by our civilization. Like the birds, we like to relax and sing at times."

Akon then lifted his head to the heavens and sang a haunting melody in a rich, deep, glorious tenor. Stirred by the beauty and romance of his voice, my eyes filled with tears of emotion. How wonderful life is when one forges a bond that transcends all other needs, an affinity and sympathy so perfect that one becomes a barometer to the thoughts and actions of a loved one.

"My voice will always sing to you, singing in the distance from another place, for we are as truly in the universe and in the skies as any of the other bright spheres we see beyond our systems. Beyond Alpha Centauri are many other bright orbs where other citizens of the universe have their being, and they sing—they sing forever to the music of the stars. The everlasting beauty of our love sings out in harmony with the celestial glockenspiels that resonate through the fathomless reaches of space. Our song will fortify the many windows of your soul, and there will be no sadness left, but only happiness in our eternal unity.

"We all have to play our part in the shaping and evolution of humankind in the cosmos. You, my dear, will need to have courage, to be brave and go back to Earth to do what you have to do. Back on Earth, your heart will not revert to the slower time beat. Your pulse rate will not remain attuned to the lower vibrations as it was in the past. Your immersion into our time continuum has altered all that. It is possible to gradually acclimatize oneself to a higher vibration merely by diet and breathing exercises. This, of course, takes time and concentration in the natural way, as we have already prepared your heart to cope with our space-time continuum. When I take you back to Earth, though, you will have to live on a drug to regulate the rhythm of your heartbeat."

I impressed the scene in my mind. I would need it for all the time to come—a source of strength for the future back on Earth, a fountain from whence my courage could be replenished during the long years ahead back on a hostile planet. The high vibratory rate within this atmosphere was affecting my heart, and I felt my pulse with alarm—the arrhythmia remained ominously high. Akon massaged the left side of my chest, under my breast, with firm, gentle pressure. He gave me an herbal tablet to swallow, and I felt better.

"We have always maintained the delicate balance of radiations between the living brains of mammals and the living stars of their systems," Akon said. "Humankind can live as long as their brain cells are regenerated by the true balance of the life-giving radiation from the star of their system, which is the center of all life. In this way, they are able to tune in and tap the vast power and influence emanating from the nucleus of the galaxy, the everlasting life force of the universe—a prodigious intelligence of light waves, continually transmitted from the depths of space.

"Humans, with their large brains, are able to contact and retain from this vast reservoir the knowledge, wisdom, intelligence and longevity that are the hallmarks of a spiritually advanced race. The human brain emits radio waves to connect with the radio waves emanating from the home star. If a star is a variable, like the Sun, the radiation bombards the planets unsteadily and the brain cells of living creatures degenerate. This is the cause of the aging process, and these creatures become aggressive and prey upon each other. They age rapidly, because the vital brain cells are affected and begin to decay. How different would the story of Earth become, if the people of that beautiful living sphere could change their attitude of mind—for an attitude of mind is a product of environment, and climatic changes can be induced and controlled.

"We are not overpopulated. We have a method of birth control that uses a simple plant that grows in the woods here. This herb is added to the diets of men and women as needed, and the effects are temporary. In fact, the herb has great health properties and is a beneficial addition to the diet. We do not believe in overcrowding or haphazard population growth, which are very retarding to mental expansion and health. Just as people of Earth moved out to other countries across their seas, so we move out to other planets within the galaxy. In this way, we retain a balance of population.

"Vibrations are most intense within Earth's atmosphere, and the minds of all living creatures and the sensitivity of plants are attuned to these vibrations. Because of the widespread swarm of humanity crowding the landmasses and cities of the planet, these vibrations are harsh and out of harmony. Such discord is most intense in the lower octaves, and resonance is most damaging to the delicate cells of the brain. This represents a major hazard to the mental health of millions of your people, and it is rapidly building up in the lower atmosphere. Supersonic vibrations of high-speed aircraft press on their brains, and although they are unheard by the ears, the danger increases in the resonance of inaudible higher octaves.

"Well, there is none of that sort of thing here, so I want to forget all about the behavior of people on that planet. I have you and my son here with me now."

Akon kissed me long and tenderly.

A great white seabird settled beside us, ruffling snowy feathers and regarding us with bright golden eyes, head aslant as it gracefully folded its vast wings into place. I stroked its head gently and gave it a piece of oat bread out of Akon's pouch. The bird fastidiously pecked it up with a delicate air of grace and then waddled off through the grass, quietly chirping to itself in contentment.

How lovely for the birds! There were no extremes of winter cold and summer heat, and no destructive storms to batter their feather-light bodies about the sky. The seasons were gentle and temperate, controlled by the scientific methods of a great and wonderful people who remained quietly within their own domain of peace, a utopia that really existed. Therefore, they did not wish to make contact with outside civilizations that could destroy their gentle way of life. Experiencing the mode of living conducted by civilizations on Earth, I understood fully why Akon's civilization kept its distance and refused to have any contact with the governments of that planet.

"Here come the horses," Akon said. "Forget about the barbarians. They will never reach our system here. We moved out of the Sun's system because of them. They are already probing onto Venus and Mars and transmitting radio signals in an attempt to communicate with us. This is a highly dangerous exercise for them, making their position known within the galaxy. There are other beings out there, ruthless and highly advanced in their science and technology, who may decide to decipher these signals and follow up the invitation in order to colonize Earth, instead of making friendly advances as Earth scientists hope. We have no intention of being involved in all that."

"Of course," I replied. "Your civilization would be destroyed if you did."

We watched a beautiful craft, glinting and flashing in the golden radiance from the three stars, skim over the top of the sea and then rise up toward the hilltop. Floating in the sparkling air, it looked ethereal as it stopped and hovered over us. It dipped down in greeting, and then flashed away again. We waved back to the people inside, and the horses nuzzled around us for oat bread.

Akon lifted me onto the back of the mare that stood quietly beside me. Her back was soft and comfortable and I buried my hands into her snowy, silken mane and gripped her warm sides with my knees. Akon vaulted onto the back of a glorious creature who had neighed and trotted up to him. We moved down the hill, across the stream, heading toward the mountains. There were no such things as bridles and saddles; the horses responded to thought and voice. The fleet-footed creatures seemed to skim over the soft sward with a very comfortable and graceful pace, jumping the smaller streams and hedges in their stride. We soon reached the foothills and the horses slowed, ambling and pacing up the slopes with a swinging motion that was quite natural and untiring for them. It was second nature for me to be on the back of a horse. All my life I had used their four legs instead of my own, as I had ridden horses since the age of one.

We reached the sheer cliff faces of rose-red rock just as the clouds cleared away, and Akon lifted me off the mare's soft and broad back. The horses went to drink from a crystal-clear stream that bubbled over smooth stones. On the bank we found a picnic tray that had been left there by Haben as he hovered over the stream in his small circular craft. He was always so thoughtful and kind, and we discovered a delicious repast prepared by Pleia's gentle hands.

While resting in a lovely dell with a vast and glorious view of land and sea, a small piece of rose rock dropped from the cliff face above and rolled against my sandaled foot. Picking it up, I held it in my hand—a piece of a beloved Meton, weathered and nurtured in the rock face, more precious to me than the most precious stones of planet Earth.

"It is for you," Akon said softly as he looked up at the rock face. "A piece of your own world, to have and to hold always—a talisman, to give you strength when you are far away. Even this planet knows you belong here, my beloved."

I placed the glowing fragment of rock in the pouch with the oat bread, covering it with soft green moss from the stream bank—and then I saw the maidenhair fern.

"Oh!" I exclaimed.

"Of course you may," Akon said, answering my thought. Very gently, he gathered up the fern with its roots and placed it in the pouch. "When we get back, I shall place the fern in a special container where it can grow and thrive. These plants live forever as we do, and you can care for it always."

"So now I have the rock, the soil, the flora—and the fauna that is within me," I whispered to Akon, my voice trembling with the depth of my emotion. "Oh, my beloved, how wonderful it all is, and you are my love and my life."

Calling the horses, Akon lifted me again onto the mare's back. We rode qui-

The fern from Meton.

etly through the lovely countryside, on through fields of waving corn and wheat that grew as natural grasses. Further on there were fields of oats and barley. Corn, or maize, grew in abundance everywhere, while various types of fruit and vegetables grew in areas set aside for such cultivation. There was never any shortage of food, and the vegetation maintained a steady rate of growth in the absence of the retarding effects of the weather or a Moon.

Luxuriance of vegetation created a high oxygen content within the troposphere, and the animal life balanced this with carbon dioxide expiration that is absorbed by the plants. There was nothing—no pollution released into the atmosphere—to deplete the vital ozone layer, which safeguarded the planet against ultraviolet radiation. The atmosphere was fresh and invigorating. One felt full of an alertness of mind and body. To become tired was unknown; one felt relaxed and completely without any nervous tension.

Vast agricultural farms supplied the fresh food necessary for the sustenance of life and health throughout the planetary system. The great spaceships also transported it to other planets, where colonists improved conditions for future generations beyond the confines of Alpha Centauri.

"For We Are the Remnant, the Descendants of these Human Beings Who Developed a Great and Glorious Civilization on Venus."

The temperate climate of Meton, and the other planets within the system, has naturally helped to evolve—to great equanimity—the minds of its inhabitants. Electric storms, which affect the emotions because of changing magnetic fields, occur beyond the equatorial zones in the southern and northern hemispheres. The vagaries of climate have been controlled, and the result is that no extremes of heat and cold intrude upon the temperate and equatorial zones of the planet. Rainfall is high, with moderate humidity because of the vast expanse of the seas. Vegetation is lush and green, covering the surface of the land; large and small islands make up the landmasses, and are inhabited throughout the equatorial regions. The polar caps of the auroral areas provide the wind patterns that temper climatic conditions over the surface of the planet. Earthquakes are unknown. The shifting of landmasses has been halted by the magnetic balance of the entire solar system, and the surface is not exposed to varied and sudden atmospheric pressures.

Every now and then, the mare I was riding picked a mouthful of swaying oat heads. She was very deft with her nimble mouth, and never slowed down from her fleet, smooth pacing. Having small stomachs, horses of this breed like to eat little and often. Akon told me that these lovely creatures were indigenous to Venus, and his civilization had brought the white horses and white cattle from Venus to acclimate on Earth and Mars prior to moving out of the Sun's system altogether. Loading the creatures into vast motherships, they brought them to Meton, where they now thrive as they did in the days of yore on Venus, the atmosphere, vegetation and seas being similar to those of the mother planet. The descendants of these white horses still exist in the strain of the Arabians on Earth. The cattle still exist in India, where they are regarded as holy creatures. The Zulu tribes also covet herds of white cattle.

We passed by a silkworm farm where thousands of enormous worms lived on vegetation within enclosed areas. Others, ready to spin, were in large containers where they proceeded to spin a lovely golden thread, fine but very strong, around a wooden peg. Nearby, the silken threads were woven into shimmering material and made up into simple patterns, and people came to choose the colors for gowns and tunics. I felt the delicate folds of my own silken gown, so smooth to the touch and pleasant to wear next to my skin.

Akon's people were a natural, constructive and energetic race, each individual doing the work he or she most loved and was suited to. Indeed, they were all individuals, no two alike, and all were completely free and happy without restrictions of any sort. How different from Earth, I thought, where people were mass-produced to conform to fashion and they all looked alike and had to think alike too; otherwise they became something apart, and were shunned by the herd.

Back home, we let the horses go and watched them gallop away toward the sea, snowy tails streaming out in the wind of their swift passage. Joyfully we embraced Pleia and Haben, who were anxiously waiting for us, knowing that the ride and exercise would hasten the birth of Akon's son.

We all sat quietly in the lovely living room to watch a scene materialize like a curtain across the room. It was a scene in history, back in time, a breathtaking vision in the electric mirage. It showed a fair-skinned people with almond eyes surveying a new planet and talking among themselves in a strange and beautiful language. The land was tropical and overgrown with lush vegetation. Great trees, festooned with creepers, encroached to the edge of broad sandy beaches where long glistening breakers crashed on the golden sands in foaming agitation that indicated a restless atmosphere. Wild creatures chattered and screamed within the dense foliage, which was alive with the sounds of teeming life, virile and ruthless in the fecundity of such a warm and humid atmosphere. The sky was dark and stormy, with long clouds scudding across the sky. Behind the people, a small circular spaceship rested on the wide beach.

"Our first scientific survey ship had just arrived on Earth," Akon said, "landing on a strange planet for the first time. The great landmasses were harsh and primitive, with many volcanoes, and the seas were tempestuous and ruthless. The planet took many, many years of taming before we could live on the surface."

The scene shifted again, showing the surface of another planet, a very different planet, with a beautiful curve of beach meeting a vast, deep blue sea, tranquil beneath a sapphire sky. The emerald green of rolling grasslands sloped away to mountains topped with rose-red cliffs. Great trees dotted the landscape, many-colored flowers carpeted the rich terrain and an elusive and haunting fragrance mixed with the tang of the vast seas. The fresh foliage and flora of the land delighted my senses, and I took deep breaths of it.

This was Venus. Its glory lived again in the electric mirage, the deep atmosphere reflecting the close and intense radiation of the Sun. The planet reflected the light out into space, with only beneficial radiation filtering through the vast ionosphere and the wide ozone layer to the surface. In this way Venus was protected against lethal radiation from its star. Cosmic dust, attracted by the Sun, formed high, noctilucent clouds around the planet, adding more light to its reflection.

Venus is a home of life in the vast void of the heavens, where there is no darkness in its slow rotation. Its proximity to the Sun keeps the upper depths of the atmosphere illuminated with a glowing twilight throughout the night.

"ONE'S MIND NEEDS TO ENCOMPASS THE ENTIRE UNIVERSE TO REALIZE AND KNOW WHAT IT IS ALL ABOUT."

Then Theton spoke in the beautiful language of his people. A translation came directly into my ears from the high back of the couch Akon and I were sitting on.

"The cradle of humankind, the mother planet, brought forth the human race out of vast, warm seas covering her surface with sapphire blue. We were spawned in the salty seas, and our blood still harbors her brine. Our life blood is but a legacy of the salty seas. It was during the early middle age of this solar system that the dawn of human life evolved. The emergence of humankind in a supernova created an adaptable species of life, retaining always a love for the seas from whence they came—the womb of our creation—with the life-giving liquid still running through our veins.

"For we are the remnant, the descendants of those human beings who developed a great and glorious civilization on Venus. They were stabilized by peace and harmony among themselves, and with nature and the universe.

"Scattered isles like emeralds slumbered in the filtered rays of the waxing Sun. A deep reflective atmosphere of cerulean sky, with snowy clouds to bring the rains of a gentle clime, gave breath to our forebears, who swam in the warm seas and breathed the fresh oxygen of the moist atmosphere. Hair or fur on the body was unnecessary, as the warm climate, stable atmosphere and tranquil seas gave protection. Long, beautiful hair on the head protected the brain from cosmic rays. The hair was full of static electricity for this reason and was blonde or golden to reflect the rays. Pubic areas of the body were also protected by hair. The original Venusians would lie out on the golden sands when coming out of the sea, to sleep during the twilight hours.

"Through eons they lived in the seas and on islands of breathtaking beauty, getting their nourishment from the plants of the seas and the land. Radiation from the star was filtered through a dense atmosphere during daylight when our ancestors spent their time in the sea. Thus there was no pigment in the skin, which has remained white and delicate, as it is with us, to this epoch in time. We have a natural longing for the sea, handed down to us through the ages. We care for our white skin against the damaging radiation of stars.

"Evolving through a peaceful existence in harmony with nature, our science and technology expanded. We explored the higher atmosphere, anxious to discover what lay beyond the high clouds of cosmic dust. Our scientists perfected skyships filled with helium to float beyond the limits of the atmosphere, where we discovered other worlds shining with the reflected light of the Sun. We then wished to explore these other worlds, and perfected spaceships to cross the far reaches of space. We reached our neighbor world—a binary system, which seemed most interesting, with the larger planet harboring life. After landing on Earth, which we showed you in the first reflection in time, we continued into space and landed on Mars, thereby encompassing the three inner planets of the solar system where the temperature range from the star permits the existence of active life as we know it.

"These three planets flourished in peace and harmony through eons of time. But ever alert to protecting their heritage in a violent universe, the scientists of this utopia detected a flaw in the rhythm of the Sun. As it aged, it became a variable star and expanded with lethal radiation in cycles of time in its path of evolution. The cycle recurs more frequently as the star ages and loses the pressure balance within.

"Our scientists traveled outward in their starships, away from the mother system, to seek a new and waxing star system to harbor the peoples of their civilization and perpetuate their race. Vast spaceships were constructed to travel the fathomless reaches of interstellar space and carry the millions of people away from the Sun's system. Our scientists found a neighboring system and they landed there, setting up their headquarters on four young planets capable of harboring life as we know it. In time, our civilization improved conditions on the remaining three planets of the system, and now we occupy the entire solar system known as Alpha Centauri.

"The spaceships we used to take our civilization to Alpha Centauri are known as motherships—they are vintage ships, but are still in use at this time. We carried the horses, cattle and other gentle types of animals in these spaceships to their new homes in Alpha Centauri, as well as many species of birds.

"The scientists left a remnant of their people on Earth to father a new race of humankind adapted to a flaring star. They maintained lands in the far northern hemisphere of the planet, as natural upheavals through the eons changed the face of the lands and the seas in the equatorial and southern regions. The descendants of these people are now so interbred and sorely affected by continuous cycles of climatic and environmental changes and extremes of weather that they are almost unrecognizable. Except for some of them here and there, they no longer bear any resemblance to the tall, golden-skinned race of humankind, with aquiline features and almond eyes, who were our forebears from Venus and who were far removed from the present savagery of the human mind in the intensity and depravity of the present time on Earth.

"Violence and annihilation will be the outcome for people of Earth, unless they change their attitude of mind. They need to become enlightened to the truths of the universe in which they live, and follow their forebears into space to find the escape route to the stars and their destiny. A harsh and precarious existence is endured by the inhabitants of Earth, where rigid social laws have to be maintained. Many would otherwise be trampled beneath the rushing feet of their avid companions on a world where politics and a primitive system still exist."

Aha, I thought as Akon began to speak. Now is the time for straight talking and the truth.

"According to Earth scientists, stellar distances are expressed in parsecs, one parsec being the distance at which the angle of parallax is one second of arc (30 billion kilometers or 3.26 light-years). The parallax of the nearest star to Earth, Proxima Centauri, is 0.76, corresponding to a distance of 1.31 parsecs or 4.3 light-years. To use the light-year, since light traveling at 3 million kilometers a second covers some 10 billion kilometers in a year, this means that the distance between Earth and Proxima Centauri is about 42 billion kilometers. Theton mentioned before, when we were in the mothership, that these stars, a triplet system, are of type G or K, similar to the Sun. This star system known as Alpha Centauri is 39 billion kilometers—or 4 light-years—from Earth. Therefore, this star system is closer to Earth than astronomers have calculated. With your present instruments, stellar distance determination is difficult even in the case of the nearer stars. Astronomers classify a star by its spectral lines, from which its intrinsic luminosity can be inferred, and hence its distance estimated from its apparent brightness in the sky.

"Twinkling stars seem to be related to starlike objects and not to extragalactic nebulae. Astronomers thought that these objects might actually be stars. A radio source lies in the direction of the constellation Centaurus, emanating from a distant galaxy of unusual mass and brightness. This galaxy possesses a nucleus equivalent to a hundred million suns, concentrated in a volume of space smaller than that occupied by your solar system. The twinkling radio source is coming from this galaxy out in intergalactic space.

"Earth scientists still cannot grasp the concept of cosmic knowledge and understanding. One's mind needs to encompass the entire universe to realize and know what it is all about. Instruments are still limited and affected by the Sun's corona. It was mentioned earlier, when we were in the mothership, that the Sun's tenuous corona extends so far from the visible disk that Earth and Mars are enveloped in it. This simply means that Earth and its atmospheric sheath are not moving in a perfect vacuum at all. The tenuous corona—the outer atmosphere of the Sun known as the ecosphere—is at a temperature suitable for the existence of advanced life. In other words, three planets—Venus, Earth and Mars—are within the temperature range of the Sun, which permits the existence of active life as we know it.

"We can see the corona encircling the Sun like a halo, the pulsing streamers of the Sun's atmosphere. Further out it becomes more tenuous and invisible. That is the Sun's outer atmosphere, or ecosphere. The corona is best observed from Earth during a total eclipse. The Sun's corona is a dense concentration of the particles that radiate to the outer regions of the solar system.

"The exosphere is the outer atmosphere of a planet. We observe all this data through the lens of our cosmic understanding; it must all be observed as a whole. It is no good observing and understanding your environment in the galaxy by what goes on in the bottom of your garden. We do not feel the effect of cosmic storms at the bottom of our garden, because we live at the bottom of an ocean of air that provides a stout shield against the rays that bombard our planet. Solar flares burst from the surface of the Sun. These flares are responsible for the solar storms that bombard the Earth with abnormal amounts of radiation. This also occurs with the stars in this system, but owing to the distance between our star, Proxima Centauri, and the binary system of Alpha Centauri (we call the entire star system a triplet system), we are not unduly affected by solar storms. The average separation between the stars in a spiral arm is eight light-years.

"Our science—and our knowledge of these distances, of course—are quite different, because our civilization and achievements are far in advance of anything known on Earth. I am outlining these simple explanations in Earth terms so that when you write this down, my beloved, the average people on Earth will have an understanding of their environment within the cosmos. Their minds are, as a rule, restricted to their backyards."

"Do you think it would help to give them more information?" I asked.

"Definitely not," Akon sternly replied. "They would only use it for political and military purposes."

"So you see," he continued, "this star that is nearest your Sun lies at a distance of more than 4 light-years, which is roughly equal to 39 billion kilometers according to Earth astronomers, as their calculations vary. Alpha Centauri is a binary system and Proxima, at 4.2 light-years, is a far-out member of the Alpha Centauri group. They calculate Alpha Centauri as being at a distance of 4.3 light-years.

"All this makes Venus and Mars very close by to Earth people, and Earth lies near the center of the Sun's ecosphere region, which gives it an advantage over Venus and Mars. There is thunderstorm activity in the atmosphere of Venus, as the upper atmospheric layers are cold, while those near the surface are very hot. We are now improving these conditions, cooling the atmosphere to surface level in order to allow these thunderstorms to produce precipitation. This, in turn, will bring moisture and the cooling of the land, and then flooding to create lakes and seas. Mars still has active volcanoes, which are the breath of life. Its riverbeds will run once more with the waters of life, when we take over these planets again. We will do so to prevent the wanton destruction that would be their lot if humankind from Earth were to take over."

"Oh," I said softly. "I am so glad."

"There is much more to tell you," Akon said, "but that must wait now."

I Had No Idea of the Time as We Keep It on Earth, but I Sensed the Time Going So Fast, So Very Fast, and I Dared Not Think of the Future. I Just Lived for the Glory of the Moving Present.

The fantastic scene shimmered away into nothing. I was stunned and overwhelmed by the magnitude of it all, and above all, by these wonderful people who had overcome their fear of the unknown and moved out into the vast reaches beyond their home system. They ventured out beyond their known ken to explore and prepare for future generations and bring the magic lease of life back to Venus and Mars.

The orange disk of Proxima Centauri lowered in the sky toward the mountains with the slow rotation of Meton. The trees cast long shadows over the emerald sward and the vast expanse of sea darkened in its blueness, but night did not come. The magnificent twin stars of Alpha Centauri rose over the sea, and the atmosphere filled with a golden light and the swelling chorus of many birds.

The fresh tang of the sea filled the room as Pleia told me, "We do not have books, but instead we keep our history in visual sound libraries, such as these magnetic rolls. When the rolls are electrified, they show the scene that you saw portrayed across the room. These rolls go back in time to when our scientists perfected such means of reflections in time, like photographing images in the atmosphere, such as thought forms and planetary scenes of the past, present and future. We can hear the hissing breath of a planet vibrating in the sound waves of time, fanning out beyond the light barrier, sounding on the harmonic cords of the heart rhythm of the parent race, and we go to gather it back into the fold."

"And that is what you are now doing to Venus and Mars," I reflected. "How wonderful to have this awareness of a planet's life, to be aware that a planet is a living entity that is entitled to care and consideration like anything else."

"And you, my dear, were ready to come out into the depths of personal experience, and you have therefore attained this privilege of being witness to other worlds beyond your own. We have affinity of mind and are closer than sisters."

Pleia put her arm around me, lifting me out of the soft couch.

"Come," she said. "I will take you to your bed. You must rest now."

We went up the gently sloping stairs to the first floor and into a room that opened off the circular balcony. Half of the circular wall of the room was open to the fresh air, and a low oval divan lay in the center of the room, covered with rose-red silk. A toilet room opened in the wall with a large sunken bath, long mirrors and exotic plants growing around the glowing walls. The sunken bath, made of mother-of-pearl, was in the middle of the room.

Pleia slipped my silken gown off and gently but very firmly laid me down on the divan, then proceeded to massage my back with long, firm strokes.

I stretched out on the firm comfort of the divan and felt every muscle in my body relax. Akon bent over me and kissed my forehead. I knew the time of birth was at hand, and I relaxed in mind and body as Akon calmly organized the birth of his son with endearing words and the massage of his healing hands. I felt the power of his hands on my body as he gently massaged my tummy and my thighs, encouraging my confidence, erasing all tension and creating an atmosphere of joy and contentment with his loving care and attention.

Gently, turning me onto my side again, he massaged my back. No pangs of contraction coursed through my thighs. There was a silence so deep as I felt Akon's hands turn me onto my back again. He tenderly stroked my hair back and told me to go to sleep. Wondering in my half asleep state where I had heard him say this before, my mind was illuminated suddenly with the vision and knowledge of our perfect unity, and I knew we had always been together through the pastures of time.

"Push down gently," Akon said. "Take a deep breath, and push again."

There was no tension, no pain, no sense of labor or strain as Akon placed my feet flat on the divan, bending my knees up and holding them wide apart. I had a sense of comfort and well-being, as if I were floating on a cushion of air, yet I was aware that I was fully dilated and ready to give birth to our son. Then suddenly, with no effort at all, just a deep feeling of achievement and pleasure, he was born gently and smoothly, coming away with the placenta. Akon extricated him from it and Pleia dried him in the scented air that was moist with the fragrance of the sea.

"A beautiful son for you both," Pleia said, placing him in my arms to suckle. "He is perfectly formed, with your golden hair and eyes. Born naturally and easily, his debut into the outside world is completely without shock to his system."

His smooth, golden skin was without wrinkles, and as I gathered his warm, naked body to my breast, Akon put his arms about us both. My beloved brought me back to the universe and the knowledge of who I am through the golden glory of love's light, and the fathomless seas of space revealed the truth of life where love and creation is the secret.

We all rejoiced in the happiness of our unity. Many friends and relatives came from far and wide to see Akon's son.

"He is unusual and very special," they said. "He will become a great scientist."

On Earth the Rhythm of My Heart Would Never Be the Same Again after Living on Meton.

My son's growing period was full of wonder for me. He gently suckled the milk of life from me, and as his beautiful white teeth formed, he turned to the natural diet we all shared. At no time did Akon and I leave him alone. He shared the music with us, he came with us on Akon's back for walks and he came with us when we rode the white horses to the mountains or bathed in the sea. The pure air and healthy climate, along with the delicious foods and water full of vitamins and trace elements, soon restored my health. Akon made us have long periods of sleep, stretched out on the comfortable divan, and my son would snuggle into my arms. He never fretted and cried as Earth babies do—he was happy and contented, but always full of life and intelligence, taking note of everything around him. Nothing escaped his discerning golden eyes and his rapidly forming intellect as he grew into a beautiful child, gentle and considerate. He slept long hours on his own divan in the room where he was born, the beautiful room open to the sky, while Akon and I spent our time together tending the gardens, the horses and the birds, playing lovely music on stringed instruments or lying together on the big divan for hours of peaceful slumber and love.

I played an instrument with a keyboard and found that I could create the most lovely music by just playing the notes in the same fashion as a piano keyboard. The white keys were made of pearl with a pink luster and the black keys of deep red garnets that looked black without light underneath. It was a lovely little musical instrument like a celesta, hand carved from the golden wood of the mountain trees, which gave it a harmonious soundboard. I loved it very much and wished I could always have one.

"Perhaps you will, my beloved," Akon would gently say.

The days were serene and glorious. Sometimes great cumulus clouds would build up, bringing rain across the land and the seas, and Akon would take us away in his planetary craft—a small replica of his scientific spaceship—to other parts of the planet and show us the beauty of the islands and vast seas. We would hover over glistening polar caps and then land on islands covered in green parklands where homes in low circular buildings gleamed in the golden daylight. We often landed on the top of one of the homes to visit friends and spend some time with them, sometimes for days. I had no idea of the time as we keep it on Earth, but I sensed the time going so fast, so very fast, and I dared not think of the future. I just lived for the glory of the moving present.

"I have attuned your heart to the higher vibratory rate emanating from the radiations of light in this system," said Akon, answering my thoughts. "It has stepped up to match the time continuum on Meton, which you are now sensing."

There were no cities or skyscrapers as Earth people know them anywhere on Meton. Homes were scattered in parklike grounds amid flowering shrubs and beds of brilliant flowers. The smooth, green lawns needed no cutting or trimming, as the grass covered the ground like a springy moss. Here was an abundance of all things needed by civilization—food, water, all materials for building, an unlimited supply of energy on tap from the atmosphere and the universe. There were no shortages of any kind, and no monetary system at all. It was a perfectly organized way of life, with an abundance of all things. The inhabitants tended and cared for all aspects of life within this great and powerful civilization. There were no films of violence, horror and murder and there were no drugs, drinking or smoking. There were no comics for children full of the horrors of life on Earth—a corrupt civilization with a past and present satiated with cruelty, slavery and a horrifying record of shooting and violence. All this type of thing, the way of life on Earth, was taboo on Meton. Nobody wanted to see it; it was unnecessary—something only for barbarians, loathsome and savage foes who howled at the gates of their neighbors.

Akon's civilization had created a utopia and kept it entirely apart from contamination by other civilizations. A way of life, a way of thinking, an attitude of mind, a high level of existence—all these things had to be protected from destruction by others less evolved. There is the vital matter of hygiene—it must not be vitiated by contact with less advanced peoples.

How lovely it was to live among these wonderful people, to watch our son grow and start running about, to hear him call me Mother. That was simply thrilling for me. There was always so much to do of great interest and excitement. It was such a pleasure to be able to create so much—so much beauty to last through time.

Sometimes Akon would take us to visit the other planets of the system. Through the eons, his people had turned them into fertile places with many lakes and seas, inhabited by people and gentle animals and with no overpopulation. Many beautiful birds, large and small, lived amongst the woods and forests, and the harmony and happiness of all the flora and fauna could be felt and sensed with delight.

Back home on Meton, we settled to quiet relaxation in our lovely circular house.

"Our son needs a name," Akon said. "A name that means something to you and something to me."

"Shall we call him Ayling?" I suggested. "His name must begin with an A like yours. And it means 'noble'—a prince of the royal blood—for indeed, he already has that bearing and manner, together with gentleness and humility."

"My beloved, so be it," Akon replied. "You have chosen well. The name sounds like our names. We shall now gather everyone here to name our son and to celebrate this wonderful occasion. Pleia dear, where are you?"

"Coming!" Pleia answered from the garden. She came inside, and they discussed plans for a celebration.

"Let's have it out in the garden," I suggested. "It's so very beautiful. I need to preserve every precious moment of my life here. Only four months of Earth time, and it is going so quickly. But then, there are no years, months or weeks here for that matter. Time is not marked off in intervals," I said with wonder in my voice. "Therefore we simply move in the stream of time, which makes us ageless."

"My beloved," Akon replied, "you are ageless now, without the restriction of months and years. Because of the stream of time on this planet, it will seem like only four months to you when I return you to Earth. Time is of no consequence here on Meton. There is no night or day, nor the marking of intervals of time. In fact, the higher vibratory frequency of light you are now immersed in will restrict the aging process of your body, and you will be younger when you return to Earth. Four months are only applicable to Earth time. The aging process in days, weeks, months and years does not apply in the higher range of frequencies, where the passage of time—and the span of human life—is so changed that the myth of Methuselah seems pale in comparison. Human beings, like the micro-atoms of light, can be stirred from their lethargy and attain eternal life through their electromagnetic nature. Through this they are able to renew themselves physically every seven years with pure thoughts and love, by simply strengthening electromagnetic energy and by adhering to that which they are.

"Time is not a factor in our lives. We live in timelessness. Our stars are eternal and constant in their output of radiation and the spiral wave-form of light, and time moves in harmonic frequency. The Sun's system is not harmonically balanced because the star itself is a variable, and because Jupiter, with its retinue of planets and satellites, is another star that is variable in its output. As a forming sun, Jupiter emits the radiation of a star, and its closer planets benefit from this output.

"We describe the Sun's system as a cluster system," Akon explained, "a solar system within a solar system. All stars and planets within a system affect one another and in turn affect all flora and fauna upon each planet. Galaxies, similarly, exert magnetic influence on all solar systems. We use these wavelengths of light for navigation purposes."

The celebration took place in Akon's home. Many luminaries of this great civilization came from as far afield as the constellations of Lyra and Cygnus. Solar systems with inhabited planets exist there, as the scientists among Akon's people have, over the eons, improved conditions there. They all loved Ayling, as his beauty as a young child was something quite remarkable. His high intelligence and perfection of manner impressed even these great people, and they wanted to take him away with them to the constellation of Cygnus.

"This is a fantastic success with a woman of a planet like Earth," they said. "We would like Ayling to visit us in our part of the galaxy. He will become a great scientist and benefit our civilization."

"Oh no, Cygnus is too far away," I told them. "It is at least 1,500 light-years from Earth to Deneb. Vega in Lyra is much closer, only about 26 light-years from Earth. Please don't take him to Cygnus. There is going to be a supernova in that constellation."

"My dear, there is no need to be upset," one of the scientists said. "We did not mean you to be. We will not take your son to Cygnus if you do not wish it. But we are very interested in your prediction of a supernova taking place in that area. We are aware of the star in question, and we believe you—your intuition and knowledge of the future is heightened with your son involved. Now that we know the truth, we must ask Akon to accompany us back to Vega to observe this very important occurrence. We have just sent a message to the home system in Cygnus to warn them to keep a watch on the star. This will mean the birth of another solar system."

I looked at Akon, and his eyes reassured me and gave me courage as I took Ayling's hand and we quietly went upstairs together. The timing of my heartbeats had started to go out of rhythm when the scientists suggested taking Ayling away to Cygnus, and now Akon would be going to Lyra. He would take Ayling with him to educate him in the mysteries of the universe, and I would be taken back to Earth where I must impart all this knowledge to a struggling humanity—and in so doing, be parted from my beloved ones.

The herbal juices helped to regulate my heart, but the stress of attempting to maintain the vibratory rate of the time continuum on Meton caused its rhythm to become worse, and I had to remain indoors within a pressurized room suitable to the timing of my heart rhythm. Akon did not wish to implant a timing device, which would have regulated my heart to the electrical frequency of Meton for all time, because I had to return to Earth and my heart's rhythm was tuned to Earth's electrical field through the influence of the Sun. But back on Earth, the rhythm of my heart would never be the same again after living on Meton. I would never regain my health either way—not by the implant of a timing device or even the implant of a living heart, because the metabolism of my whole being had been changed and subjected to a higher frequency in a different time dimension, from which it could never recover. The rhythm of the heartbeat varies in changed time field conditions as the body tries to maintain normal circulatory pressure within the atmosphere of alien planets, where light and gravitational pressure vary.

"HEARTS ARE TIMEPIECES FOR THE ELECTRICAL VIBRATORY RATE OF-EACH INDIVIDUAL WITHIN THE ENVIRONMENT OF BIRTH."

How worthwhile it all was, though, I thought. How wonderful. I had really lived to the fullest as the divine essence of truth encompassed me. The golden glory of Akon's love and Ayling's love would remain with me forever—never, ever to change.

The trees outside were enveloped in the hazy mist of their respiration as they released an abundance of oxygen into the atmosphere. How fresh and invigorating it was. All life responded and grew in abundance within these harmonious environs. To be a part of this life would be a joy forever, and to tune in to this essence, to become one with it, would always be my privilege. I knew that when events and happenings on Earth became too much for me, I could always escape within myself and tune into Akon and my son on their beautiful planet, beyond the restrictive time field of Earth, and they would know of my need for them.

My departure to return to the soil of Earth held a poignant moment: leaving my golden boy. He would grow up quickly with Pleia and Haben. Ayling was a little boy whose gentle eyes already had the look of distance, the faraway look of wisdom—already he was seeing beyond the limited horizons of earthbound people. Within his eyes was the knowledge and wisdom of the universe—a four-dimensional vision into the hearts of humankind. He was a little boy conceived by love, nourished and quickened within my body on Earth, born on another planet beyond the light barrier to acclimatize his heart to a higher frequency rate in the electromagnetic waveform, where the flow of time and the speed of light interact harmonically with the stars of his home system. He would grow up much more quickly than Earth children, and he would not experience the darkening hand of death.

There was no sadness or emotion as Akon's spaceship flashed away from the lovely planet. I knew I would be back again soon. I was only going away to Earth for a while to do the work I had to do—to bring the truth of the universe to the people there, to help expand their consciousness, to make them aware of their existence in an energetic universe, to make them understand why they were born, why they are who they are and why they must overcome their continuous strife.

The darkness of space filled the viewer, except where bright stars gleamed and passed in the flow of time. Sheron concentrated with relaxed confidence on the course of the spaceship, his mind attuned to the radiation of Earth's star, using telepathic waves of alpha rhythm—brain waves of a particular frequency—for celestial navigation. His handsome face was a study in complete composure, with a lock of fine chestnut hair across his high forehead giving him the appearance of a legendary god in deep thought as his golden eyes met mine in a flash of understanding.

The bluish radiation from the Sun filled the viewer and I saw its retinue of planets spaced out, reflecting the light of their star. Only Jupiter shone with an internal radiation, its planets and satellites bathed in and reflecting its light and that of the Sun. Jupiter is a solar system within a solar system, where forms of life have their being, similar to elsewhere, and their way of life attuned to the finer shell of atmosphere around their small planets.

Suddenly, before I could say anything, we were in the region of Earth's exosphere, then in the ionosphere. In that instant I saw the sky, soft blue and dappled with white clouds, as the spaceship smoothly changed frequency rate and appeared, hovering, over the mist-shrouded hills of Natal. After a moment, we landed gently beside the winding mountain track. Zulu men and women, returning to the homestead after a day in the fields, scattered with fright like a covey of quail. Their shouts of alarm could be heard far away on the mist-covered mountain.

"The sky wagon from Mdedelele[1]," I heard them call to one another in Zulu through the viewing lens, as the winding mountain track lost itself in white mist. A telephone post stood gray and ethereal on the far bank of the track.

"Mdedelele" echoed through the hills. "Make room for me." The mountain of Cathkin pushed into the main range of the Drakensberg, and the wagon of the sky had returned, pushing into the atmosphere. The descriptive words of the nearby Zulu faded in the distance when the viewing lens was switched off.

I had no fear of the Zulu. Only the white men would harm me to get at the knowledge in my mind. When I was a child, a prancing Zulu warrior had saved my life by picking me up out of the path of a vicious snake and placing me on his shoulder as it rose up to strike at me. The great cobra buried its fangs in his cowhide shield as he flung it to the ground, and he killed the snake with his assegai[2]. Chanting a war song, he ran with me on his shoulder back to the house and into the arms of my mother, who had had a premonition that had brought her out to look for me. My white nanny scolded me and put me to bed for riding on the shoulders of a black savage!

The wind stirred in the swirling mist and seemed to penetrate the Earth as the long green grass flowed in waves to its touch. Such is the wind of Earth, blowing as it has always blown throughout all time. I could sense it howling round the dome of the spaceship in its attempt to gain a

---

1. *Cathkin*
2. *A spear of hard wood tipped with iron.*

foothold on the smooth and shiny surface. Akon moved to the wall on the leeward side, and the door slid open. The wind could not reach within the cabin because it was expelled away by the push of pure air within.

Only when we stepped out on the hull could we feel again the blast of Earth's wind against our bodies. It ripped at my hair like a live thing. Spawned by a wilderness of magnetic imbalance and the vibrations of violent thoughts, it pushed its strength against the mountainside in the brute-force method of all things on this planet. I took a breath of the dust-laden atmosphere, and I choked and coughed.

Akon had his all-in-one suit on so that it covered his head and face, and even the slits for his eyes were covered with an invisible material. I had changed back into my cashmere twinset and tartan kilt, my knee-high stockings and walking shoes, and I had tied a scarf over my head for warmth.

"Breathe slowly and not deeply at first," advised Akon. "Always stay in the fresh air, and gradually you will adapt again. Although your heart will not retain Earth-time rhythm anymore, the tablets I have given you will maintain an even rhythm for your heart if you take one each year. Your heart is not strong, and the effect of the time change will always be felt. Hearts are timepieces for the electrical vibratory rate of each individual within the environment of birth."

"Is there any way to ensure lasting and natural heart transplants?" I wondered.

"Indeed yes," said Akon. "It can be done by matching a heart with the same time-beat, rhythm and vibratory electrical pulse rate, just as blood types need to be matched for a transfusion. At the moment I have an electronic timing device attached to my chest to regulate the rhythm of my heartbeat in this changed time field condition, so that I can maintain normal circulatory pressure within this atmosphere. This device is embedded within the suit I am wearing, and it allows me to move freely outside of my spaceship when we have landed. We do not perform actual physical heart transplants, though, as we have found this to be quite unnecessary and contrary to nature. All we need is a device to control the pulse rate, as the heart is merely a pump that needs to work efficiently all the time."

"Then why couldn't I have a device to regulate my heartbeat in changed time-field conditions?" I said.

"My dear one, your heart is unstable. It would fly into a wild tachycardia. We have already taken the precautions that we can. There is nothing more to be done."

"Nothing is just handed to one on a plate," I replied. "For the real things in life, the things that really matter, one must know how to behave and be courageous enough to carry on."

I felt myself slipping into dire devastation of aloneness that nothing could ever alleviate, a dreadful sense of abandonment on the soil of a hostile planet. I checked it, though, before my senses could give full rein to it.

No, I thought, there is nothing more to be done. It has all been so worthwhile, so wonderful, no matter what price I must now pay with my health. Akon has told me what to expect and of the suffering to come before I can find peace.

"It depends on you, my beloved," he said, answering my thoughts. "Only through dire experience and deprivation do we achieve spiritual advancement. But remember always that my love will be with you forever. Our telepathic link remains on the alpha rhythm between our brains. And this physical parting is only temporary. Our son, Ayling, will come to fetch you home again. Now, you must go back to care for your Earth family."

He removed his mask, and kissed me with a lingering magic.

"My beloved, I will always take care of you and watch how you fare," he whispered. The wind tore at us, and after a moment, he put the stretch-mask back on.

"I shall live only for you," I softly replied, "and my love for you will give me strength."

The MG appeared from the open hold, suspended in a beam of white light that gently deposited it on the dusty track facing uphill. As the wide opening in the hull closed silently, I caught a fleeting glimpse of Sheron within—a last wave of the hand and a flash of white teeth.

Akon stood still and watched as I climbed into the MG. I drove the car slowly up the track to get out of range of the spaceship. I switched off the ignition and engaged the handbrake. Opening the door, I got out and looked back. Akon was gone. The spaceship was sealed. As I watched, the ship started to pulsate and glow with an unearthly radiance in the lowering mist, and then it too was gone. The beautiful starship was gone, and my life and my love had gone with it.

I returned to the car and drove on up the dusty track over the mountaintop, back to the farmstead nestling in the trees on the north side facing the mountains of the Dragon. A warm welcome and a happy greeting always awaited me, no matter what time of day or night I arrived and no matter how long I had been away or where I had been. I had come back again—that was enough. My room was always ready, with the bed turned down. Old Muti hovered in the kitchen with a steaming silver pot of tea and fresh honey from the hive, and some of his special whole-wheat scones with Jersey butter.

Chapter 7

THE NATURE OF THE UNIVERSE

T hings had changed back on the farm. My sister's health was failing, and Jock had had another heart attack. He could no longer take part in all the activities he had been used to. It was sad for them. Both of them had always been very active in social and sporting events, with many friends everywhere. These friends, though, in a manner peculiar to Natal, were insular and wrapped up in their own affairs, and they seemed oblivious to the needs of others. Jock and May had always done so much for others. They were unselfish and generous, so different from the people around them. The beautiful estate was left more and more to the care of the Zulu manager of the farm area. Old Muti interfered, trying to run the estate his way.

David and I stayed on for a while to help, but I sensed that May and Jock would not be here much longer. I could foresee the beginning of their transcendence. They would soon be bound for the realm where the mysteries of birth, life and death reveal the truth of their substance within the divine power of the universe, where light rules the destiny of humankind.

No sadness cast its shadow across the rolling foothills of the Drakensberg. Only a paean of joy, in tune with the infinite universe of light, illuminated the craggy peaks. It created a connection with our neighboring solar system beyond the light barrier, where humankind of Earth seek and find the light of eternal life and the divine truth of their existence in other realms that testify to worlds beyond Earth.

159

The farm homestead lay shimmering in the morning sunlight and the delightful pungent smell of gumwood smoke filled the still air. I wondered what would become of all this beauty, where peace and quiet rested like the sunlight over the trees and mountain slopes. I thought of the great hump of Flying Saucer Hill, where Akon had told me of the magic qualities of light as we lay together in the long, seeding grass of the mountain slope and looked into the mysterious ice-blue of the sky as the hills tumbled away into the shadowed land of Natal. Our place of meeting was passing on in time.

Now I sensed that a new cycle of metamorphosis would emerge to show them the way to eternal life. No longer could events and happenings on Earth strangle and suffocate me, or rend my feelings to shreds with the knowledge of the truth of a planet with its people still within the dire throes of a lower evolutionary scale. People must first breathe in before they can breathe out, and live, and burst the shell of darkness.

Jock died suddenly one night, passing into Death's brief shadow—as the lifeless mealie-pit shrivels in death before moving on into a new cycle of vibrating life energy. His serene face told me he had found the truth of eternal metamorphosis. The force of continuing creation was now released within him as when the cycles of time return to pure form in a star, a cloud, a bird or a human being.

Nothing ever happens by chance, and the divine spark of life energy had delivered itself up to the great current of nature and returned to the universe as all things do. Death is a cycle in time—of change, of rebirth in life—and the flames of life and death flicker on through all existence. We sense this flickering flame of existence within the unfathomable depths of the universe, where we are all infinitesimal parts of the whole.

All is change of movement through cycles of time. All of creation plays this game of change. If we remain the same, we begin to disintegrate with time and lose our beauty, because the gift of metamorphosis is lost. And unlike the mealie-pit, the spark of life energy shrivels too, and cannot live again through the cycles of time. We need to reach the center of the universal force on a frequency wave where light responds to our vibrations in that instant of time we know as death. Only in this way are we permitted to continue within the energetic electrical cycle of that magic lease we sense as life. The energy vibrations of our being, where our dreams materialize, is quite separate from the brain. It is these energy vibrations that live on in the eternal spectrum of light beyond the darkness of death.

A few months later, my sister followed Jock. In her brief encounter with death, she too passed through the time cycle of metamorphosis into the eternal energy of life. Death is a part of life and life is a part of death— we must all experience its shadowy touch, as it is a part of the universe. Like a star, your physical body gradually decays and degenerates away, burns itself out, and the shell around one that protects the soul energy within falls away. But the real you, that divine spark, the life field, moves on into infinite timelessness in cyclical patterns, retaining a race memory within the subconscious as each life cycle occurs. You reject chaos and retain a highly organized life system that harmonically interacts with all living things and the environment. An intricate web of continuous communication connects all life throughout the universe into one vast, spinning system, and we are all part of the whole.

We are all a part of this eternity, and as our life fields evolve in harmony without chaos, the cells of our bodies cease to degenerate. The waxing and waning of all stars and planets and the rhythm of the Earth affect our life fields. We are very sensitive living sundials, responding to the star of our system. When we find the meaning of eternal life, we will be able to achieve all things, as Akon's civilization has done.

There is so much more to living in the universe than just the nuts-and-bolts approach of the man in the street or the understanding of the average scientist. Most people have absolutely no conception of what the universe means—to them it is just a random chaos. But they cause the chaos by not communicating with their environment and the universe. Instead, they destroy, thus creating an unbalanced effect within their environment that ripples outward beyond the solar system.

Life is inherent in cosmic forces. As we live and think, so the universe responds to us. This is prayer—our life fields, or auras, carry an electrical charge, attracting negative ions to us for more stimulation. In this way our life fields remain positively charged and attract the negative particles. Retaining communication and unity with the universe is the secret of life—our galaxy, the Milky Way, whose energy interacts harmonically with neighboring galaxies and galaxies beyond, and on into intergalactic space, ad infinitum. Wave patterns create harmonic chords that can be read like a score of music, and the illusion of matter is strung together with electromagnetic and nuclear forces of light.

Micro-atoms are organized, and when they are in living vibrations, they constantly repair and replace themselves. Feeding on harmony, they recognize and respond to the universe and its light energy. In this way, our beings become one with the cosmos, and we can find eternal life within the same natural frequency where resonance in sympathy maintains our connection. As light waves carry information to us, we respond according to our harmonic evolution in the octaves of time. The time continuum exists throughout galactic space, in the medium where galaxies are formed and have their being within the electromagnetic waveform of eternal light. We are an integral part of all this, and as we attain the ability of positive thinking it will bring us into contact with the cosmic intelligence.

There Are Some of Us, Though, Who Are Still in Touch with the Galactic Directory and Can Ask for Help to Stop the Rot of This Civilization.

We need to understand the light of the universe. The eternal truths of life await our perception and consciousness in the realization of seven dimensions, where humankind is not unique. Then we will be able to traverse these parallel waves, where spaceships traveling in curved space can meet and fuse at a moment in time that is a point where all lines come together.

The answer to space-flight propulsion has been solved by Akon's civilization. The mathematical formula to control gravity has been in use within their spaceships for eons, and light emanates from these great starships as a secondary manifestation of gravity waves. They have discovered its nature and its magical properties, and have worked out a formula to harness its energy for the benefit of their civilization. Gravity waves radiate outward from the nucleus of our Milky Way galaxy, interacting with all forms of matter, keeping the stars and planets in their places by pushing them outward in the everlasting circle of speeding light that forms the vast rotating lens of our galaxy.

Gravity is the push from the hub of the flattened spiral of the cosmic storm that is our galaxy. These waves are oscillating at frequencies thousands of megacycles beyond the visible light spectrum. Due to this high frequency, their general force is attractive, and electromagnetic waves react with the electrical charges and currents created within the field differentials of the spaceship's propulsion systems.

Light exists throughout our galaxy, interacting harmonically with the electromagnetic waveform, the tempic geometric and the resonating, binding force of gravity—the forces of the universe that form the unified field of cosmic energy. Earth scientists still have trouble measuring it, and do not seem to be aware of this, yet this is the basis of all life throughout the universe. Without the unified field, we would all fly apart and end in chaos.

Expansion of thought will come in the wavelength of time when the insight of humankind has reached a deeper and more spiritual level. At the present time, they are exiled on a speck of a planet out on a limb of the Milky Way galaxy, isolated in the cosmos, not knowing what they are or how they originated. Wholeness is attained within a star, a planet, a spaceship or flying saucer. A complete circle retains the wholeness of the universe or galaxy in which we all have our being. Only by becoming whole oneself, as a minute particle of the universe, can one give form to that inaccessible reality known as truth. The collective unconscious of this world is no longer in tune with the universe. The practice of religions in the East and West only continue out of habit, and they have ceased to produce any results.

Overwhelming masses of people swarm over the surface of this planet, creating an image of quantity without quality. This submerges the individual, who alone must think thoughts that are capable of transforming this world. The individual is in danger of perishing in a mass-produced world where all are alike and think alike. In nature, all forms of life are different, retaining their own individual patterns of behavior and thought while remaining a part of the universe. The vibrations of nature weld all life into wholeness, as individual particles contribute to the wholeness of the atmospheres of planets.

People of this planet lost contact with the universe thousands of years ago in Earth time. They are now accelerating toward the total destruction of nature and the environment. This is why they can expect nothing but chaos. The gap now is narrowing to less than thirty years in time for the survival of the planet and the way of life they have been softened to.

Through stupidity and ignorance, they are destroying their natural environment, causing Earth to become a barren world devoid of beauty and life. Other so-called civilizations have done this on other planets, when they lost touch with the universe, or galactic directory.

Some of us, though, are still in touch with the galactic directory and can ask for help to stop the rot of this civilization. We are family, and can turn in need to the advanced people residing in the solar system of Alpha Centauri in the constellation of Centaurus, who fathered humankind on this planet eons ago and farmed us out here, entrusting the planet to our care. We have now abused the sacred trust left to us by our forebears, who moved out into interstellar space to found a new civilization beyond the time barrier to preserve and guard the environment of our universe against other, hostile civilizations.

AS THE MIND ABSORBS THE FOURTH DIMENSION OF THE SPACE-TIME CONTINUUM, ONE BECOMES AN EVOLVED HUMAN BEING WITH UNDERSTANDING AND LOVE OF ALL THINGS.

If developed as a duplication of nature, science and technology will know no bounds. There will be no energy shortages. Motivation systems can be tapped in abundance and without cost from the universe. This will facilitate construction and overcome all traffic and pollution problems across the entire planet. It will also simplify the interplanetary and interstellar travel that will take us to the furthermost stars.

These secrets still elude scientists on Earth. Our scientists seek the clues to the natural energy of the universe with every available method of scientific research and investigation within their grasp, yet they overlook one simple clue. Earth is a living, breathing entity. Right under their big, clumsy feet, the planet moves in orbit with perturbation, inhaling and exhaling, expanding and contracting like a variable star, creating continuous life. Throughout space, on the surface of other Earths, it is the same—all have the magnetic stuff of life, gravity and light. All are within the whole.

Gravity research presents tremendous and challenging information, undreamt of in present-day science and physics, where the limit of knowledge is bound and restricted to a formula of narrow and rigid conformity. This galactic force, as yet not understood, pervades our very lives, binding us all together as an integral part of the whole and involving us all into an open dialogue with the universe.

Cosmic energy exists throughout our galaxy—a great spiral system of hydrogen gas clouds filled with stars and planets. Galaxies have always been. They are born from electromagnetic vortices within the minimum temperature of the void and commence to spin and form vast spiral or vortex storms, in the center of which enormous pressure will arise. As the hydrogen fog cloud evolves into a compact galaxy, heat is generated by the micro-atoms that are unable to penetrate the minimum temperature of intergalactic space. Spinning with tremendous velocity, an eye or nucleus is formed in the center, and the young galaxy becomes big-hubbed, with gas clouds spinning toward the center. As the galaxy ages, its rotation flattens it out into a flying-saucer-shaped E7 galaxy, and then into a spiral whose arms are formed and filled with stars and planets. Dust-belted, the galaxy evolves and star formation continues within the halo shock wave as it sweeps through the utter blackness of the minimum-temperature void of intergalactic space. The same process occurs when an eddy forms in the gas clouds, generating a more intense and compact vortex that becomes a star.

Among the hydrogen atoms, many micro-atoms will be compressed and explode with the high temperature. In this way helium is formed. The greater the pressure and heat of the micro-atoms, the more explosions and elements are formed, and the hydrogen fog cloud grows into a spinning star, radiating light to the outermost limits of its system. At those limits, planets form as smaller vortices triggered off by electricity from the parent vortex. The cells of the dust cloud bud forth all around their mother star, springing out in new heat explosions as the micro-atoms of light are condensed further, forming vibrating matter that periodically emits magma and heat residue in the form of volcanic eruptions in geometric relation to the time and light emanation of the mother vortex. Some are so close that they fuse with the mother star or with each other, forming larger planets, until the entire vortex storm settles down to a vibratory rate of harmonic interaction. Life is triggered by electricity within planetary environments as life-giving gases and atmosphere spew forth from a planet's magma. Anomalies in gravity from the parent star release magma in atomic explosions of varying intensity—the release of a star's lifeblood—enabling us all to be created out of stardust.

Gravity waves push against the surface of Earth, whose mass and density depend on the magma within—the source of all light and life. Gravity sweeps outward from the nucleus of the spinning disk of our galaxy, exerting a pressure on all nebulae, stars and planets. As our Milky Way galaxy settles down in its vibratory rate, seven spiral arms are being formed and filled with solar systems where millions and millions of planets harbor life.

Our universe is everlasting, creating the light of eternity within its electromagnetic field. Light, heat and life are created in the atmospheres of planets, and in our galaxy's orbital speed and rotational velocity around the meta-galaxy—a prodigious system within the depths of intergalactic void, the limitless reaches of outer space. There, the minimum temperature controls the lives of galaxies as they orbit in continuous momentum, in ever-widening circles around the meta-galaxy's electromagnetic hub.

We are all electric beings within an electromagnetic universe of light that has always been and will always be. It forms and multiplies, cell upon cell throughout the infinite void, when micro-atoms, the ultimate particles, vibrate in substance to which we are attuned. All things take shape relative to this planet, whose radius has a geometrical connection with time, light and gravity. Electricity triggers the birth of galaxies, stars and planets. Gravity is created by the vortex spin of all elements in nature. So the spiral system continues, only protected from chaos and entropy by the void of minimum temperature beyond the light barrier.

Humankind is born to strife on Earth, as the eternal struggle for existence manifests within the two-dimensional sphere on the surface of the planet. Territorial gains for food and living space become of primary importance, and humankind becomes violent and aggressive in an attempt to protect their domain or to seek further territory for the expanding population. Restrictive areas of living cause humans to become more aggressive and violent, and the fear of losing their domains motivates their actions.

When humans are able to escape from the two dimensions of length and breadth and follow the spiritual awakening into the freedom of height in the third dimension, where there is no restriction of territory or time, they can then become gentle and humane, and seek the wider field of space. As the mind absorbs the fourth dimension of the space-time continuum, one becomes an evolved human being, with understanding and love of all things. Finding the meaning of life and why one exists as an individual brings one in tune with the universe. Then we can communicate through telepathy in the time variation of interstellar space.

We can all achieve the calm serenity of the eternal presence within that divine spark of intelligence that pervades the entire universe. Harmony with all is found in love, with civilizations from other realms beyond the visible light barrier to which our eyes are attuned. We are born of this universe that consists of energy and matter vibrating in varying frequencies. As we expand our consciousness, we become aware of different frequencies of attainment, where the eternal truths of life await our perception and realization of the atomic-harmonic numbers of the cosmos.

Treading through the deep waters of personal experience where dangers lurked in the darkness of ignorance, I witnessed other realms beyond our world. I found the truth of supreme happiness and eternal life with a man from another world. He remains the only reality to me—within this world where the inhabitants still believe in the illusion of their singular existence within the inhabited universe.

Having been through the fires of experience and attainment—suffering the hardships of material want in a grabbing world like Earth—brought me fortitude and endurance, courage and loyalty to an ideal of life beyond the confines of this solar system. Akon's thoughts direct me through the dangerous highways of life among people of Earth, where my work now aspires to the ideal of a better world for all people.

No distance is too great for the alpha rhythm to travel between the brains of soulmates and offspring whose lives sometimes part in the quest of ultimate unity and harmony within our living universe. These telepathic waves flash through the far distances, where gravity rules the lives of planets, to another home of life—to my beloved Akon and our son, Ayling, who was conceived on this home of life but was not born on this planet. Not for him the hazards of rocket-propelled spaceships encasing their pilots like coffins. Not for him to travel the stars wrapped in the swaddling cloth of a spacesuit and be packed like a sardine in a tin can in an endeavor to conquer space and the unknown environment beyond.

What would happen to David and me now that my heart was affected by the change in time frequencies? Where would the money to live on come from? I was divorced from David's father, and my daughter from a previous marriage was living in London as she completed her medical studies. The farm was sold and strangers took over, and David and I were completely alone.

Money to live is vital on this planet, so we decided to return to Johannesburg. We drove down the track in the MG—David and I, Susan and Vicky—while covetous eyes still watched from the road in the valley where a large American car remained parked by the boundary gate. A lone Harvard droned in the sky in the wake of a storm. The clean atmosphere of the mountains was beginning to develop bands of smoke haze.

Back in Johannesburg, we found a home and I got a job with a leading bookseller, while David went to day-school and excelled in all he did. But there was no fresh air in the basement of this great bookshop, and my heart condition became worse. I struggled on, however, and the bank would help me as long as I had a steady income. There was nothing left for us now in Natal, the land of my birth, where relatives of mine were settled in safe security on vast acres of rolling grasslands. I felt homesick, and a deep sadness entered my heart as the thought shivered through my mind. Only the African side of my adopted family offered us a home in the dry, open spaces of the Transvaal. I loved them for that, and would never forget their thoughtful gesture.

The fresh breeze of the highveld swept my scarf into my eyes as I crossed Commissioner Street from the bookshop. Suddenly I felt stifled by it all—the crowds of white and black people thronging the street and all the close-packed, noisy, smelly traffic. I felt suffocated by it all and sensed the urgency to get out of this warren of a city with all its devastating noise and bustle. I had to escape back to the Drakensberg. When David's school broke for the holidays, I asked for leave and it was granted, as I had worked long and hard.

The light of dawn flushed the eastern sky as David and I, along with Susan and Vicky, headed south in the MG, away from the enfolding wings cast about me by the covetous thoughts of men. The hue and cry would follow me to the farms as the security net cast its subtle and domineering tentacles to subjugate my freedom. They didn't know about Cathkin yet, however, where we could be lost forever in the mountains and only the sea wind would rustle through the long grass, bringing the breath of eternity in its damp fragrance.

So, away to the open spaces and the far reaches of the sky, away to the freedom of the mountains where I could hear my beloved's voice calling in the lofty distances. His voice was singing in my heart as we moved with the wind from the wide open spaces of the Transvaal to the land of shadows in Natal, a distance of well over 300 miles. The MG responded to my touch on the open road, her perfection of performance maintained for all time after Akon's work on her engine.

The great mountains of the Dragon shielded our passage as we branched off along a shortcut through Zulu lands. Cathkin beckoned us on with a clarity of atmosphere and grandeur of scenery. A sudden wave of longing saddened my eyes as I thought of my beloved. I recalled the fragrance of the glorious countryside from whence he comes, where the sea breeze plays with the fronds of maidenhair ferns that grow in profusion on the sunlit mountainsides, their delicate tracery of shiny black stems bending and waving to the sea's breath. I thought of my own lovely fern, given to me by Akon on Meton, and how it was now growing well in my home, acclimated to the dry air of the highveld and nourished by love and care. As I thought of these things, the fragrance of Meton's seas filled my senses, and I knew Akon was near.

I stopped the MG on the side of the road and we got out to watch the sky. To the south, enormous thunderheads reared up into the depths of blue, glistening white like great cauliflower heads, clearcut and brilliant. Suddenly there was a flash in the sky. I took my box camera and pressed it against my chest to steady it as I pointed the lens to the top of the thunderclouds. As I did so, Akon's flat, domed spaceship suddenly appeared in the blue sky. It hovered against the great cloud bank, slowly losing height. In that instant, another spaceship appeared against the sky, moving with tremendous velocity, and I pressed the shutter release.

As the ship flashed down into the heavy cumulus of the cloud bank, I ran across the road and up the slope. When I reached the hilltop, the spaceships were gone, and the cumulonimbus spread out across the sky from the south. Akon's spaceship appeared again, and I took a series of photographs as it hovered and banked around in the sky. My reflex with the simple Brownie Box camera was as instantaneous as the spaceship's appearances—it had to be, or I could not have taken a single picture.

A streak of lightning, a blue-white ribbon, darted from hilltop to cloud, and the crash of thunder died to silence before the hills could echo in answer. Triggered into life by the electricity generated within its heart, the fully aroused cumulonimbus—composed of cells that grow, fuse and multiply—moved with its animal-like nature over the hills. I realized that the cloud was repaying my thought with a tingling sensation over my scalp. Positive charges swarmed upward from the ground, using my body as a conductor, to meet the negatively charged leader coming from the cloud, as the earth charge leaped up through the ionized tunnel prepared in the atmosphere by the cloud leaders. Instantly I jumped from the rock on which I was standing, flattening myself in the grass, and rolled down the slope in the nick of time, as the return stroke from the earth shot up through the ionized tunnel to the cloud base, shattering the hardened rock. With the sound of a cracking whip, the air in the channel expanded in a sudden and terrible explosion, and shock waves sent me rolling further down the steep slope, knocking the breath out of my body.

As was my habit, I had put the camera back in its case and strapped it across my shoulder instead of placing it on the rock beside me. The leather strap had broken during my tumble down the hill, but it was otherwise unharmed. As I retrieved the camera, another return stroke flashed with an awful crack from the shattered rock. There was a crashing explosion as the tremendous heat in the lightning's channel expanded in waves of terrific sound.

I had had enough. I ran to a large outcrop of rock ledges and sheltered beneath the largest of them, just as a curtain of rain and hail roared across the veld. I trembled with nervous reaction, and my heart went into a wild tachycardia. It was completely out of rhythm, and I felt death touch my heart as the crack and crashing explosion of lightning return-strokes continued.

Akon's craft as photographed by the author.

I was not alone in my haven. Birds of all kinds had sheltered there, and they fluttered and twittered in apprehension and uneasy disquiet. A reedbuck came bounding out of the murk of driving hail to nestle beside me, its ears twitching as each lightning crack sounded dangerously close. The calmness and warmth of the reedbuck quieted my heart, and I lay back with my arm over its back as the buck watched me with large, soft brown eyes.

After some time, the explosive turbulence died away. We all came out of the shelter, the birds ruffling their feathers and strutting unafraid about my feet. The reedbuck remained still, though, so I sat down again, resting my back against the wall of rock. I needed to rest, and I knew David and the dogs would be safe in the MG. As I sat, I thought about something strange that had happened some weeks before. A major in the British Army had called on me in my cottage in Parktown, and while we were having tea, there was an interruption at the door. I answered it to find a stranger standing there.

"Good day, lady," the stranger said. "A gray Ford Zephyr that was parked outside your gate has run away into Empire Road. I watched it pull up on the opposite pavement about a mile down. It went along the road and through the traffic as if it were guided—it was very uncanny. Motorists coming in the opposite direction nearly crashed into each other in frightened surprise when they saw that car going along the road without a driver—just going straight past them, then turning up the pavement and remaining stationary between the trees. It even missed the trees!" he ended, with a cry of amazement.

"Perhaps someone was guiding the car," I replied quietly.

"Oh no, lady, that's too much."

The stranger hurried away to the gate. As he put his hat on and glanced back at me, I saw fear in his eyes.

"Good gracious!" said the Major. "I must have forgotten to put my handbrake on."

And he dashed out to rescue his car.

I later learned that the Major was a high-ranking officer in British Intelligence who had been on General Montgomery's staff. He was a very sensitive and highly intelligent man, and a famous artist as well, who had come to South Africa to give a lecture to the Air Force. I felt sure now, though, under the circumstances, that the Chief had sent him to look after me. With that thought, I felt a glow of warmth that restored my confidence.

The reedbuck suddenly jumped up and bounded away down the grassy slope. There was a rush through the grass and the dogs found me, happiness shining in their eyes. David treaded quietly through the veld behind them in his rubber-soled shoes.

The Sun sets early beyond Cathkin, the peak casting long shadows over the hills. A cold, russet light touched the tops of the grass-mantled slopes, and the ever-changing mountain darkened the tumbling foothills. We sped on in the MG to the haven of the hostel to await Akon's coming. I hoped he would come soon. Although his spaceship was in the skies of Earth, perhaps he would not land. I only had three weeks leave from work before I would have to return to Johannesburg—the time factor on this planet crushed me again with its impact. This was our livelihood here, and I had David, the dogs and the MG to think about, as well as my home and the few precious possessions that gave us some comfort and beauty to live with.

But Akon did land! Suddenly one afternoon, his great spaceship was there. There was nothing in the clear sky and then it appeared in all its beauty, hovering close to the ground and gently landing. Completely unnoticed, the ship suddenly appeared in Earth's time field. Only I saw it. I ran to meet Akon. The halcyon days with Akon sped by. At night he would put me to sleep with his healing hands, and my heart returned to its normal rhythm again. We remained in the sanctuary of the mountains, and there was complete peace and happiness. My life had become whole once more in its unity with Akon, as it had when we had created another life to complete this wholeness.

One morning, as I awakened in the glow of sunlight, Akon was gone from my side. I looked up into the higher atmosphere and saw his spaceship moving upward, surrounded by a vast condensation cloud. Still in Earth's time frequency, the spaceship glowed with a deep golden amber inside its departure field. And then it was gone, leaving behind a vast rotating cloud, its top smoothed off into a cap cloud by the frigid heights and its base like a wake of lines of magnetic force within the atmosphere.

The great circular cloud remained in the higher reaches of the sky for the rest of the day, changing and forming into high cirrocumulus with a base of altocumulus. The wind patterns moved it gradually across the sky as cirrostratus, and it caught the golden-red rays of the Sun, creating a covenant of color made of ice crystals in the high, milky cobweb veil.

Akon was gone, back into the fathomless reaches of space beyond our solar system, away into those fathomless distances of velvet space. He was heading for the great blue-white star known on Earth as Vega in order to make a scientific surveillance of that distant star. Our solar system was moving toward Vega's hard brightness too, but the primordial plasma of the universe guided Akon's spaceship through the many frequencies of time.

Galaxies rotating eternally in the uncharted void of intergalactic space give out a life impulse that is picked up by the sensitive instruments in Akon's spaceship. These instruments monitor the life cycles of galaxies, stars and planets and detect the amount of plasma within a solar system. The plasma output of a star is important for a system of planets, particularly for a star like the Sun with its sunspot cycles, which are affected by the movements of its planets.

Jupiter, as a small star, triggers sunspots by increased magnetism when it is in a favorable position. This in turn affects Earth's atmosphere, causing weather changes as low-pressure troughs cross geometric regions of the planet's surface. Vast climatic upheavals can occur. The planet can

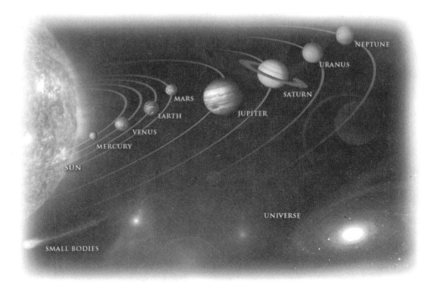

also trigger earthquakes on Earth by disturbing the equilibrium of the Sun, because our planet is completely affected by what happens to the Sun. We here are dependent on the star of our system. The Sun controls our atmosphere, our weather and our climate, and when Jupiter, the second waxing star of this system, aligns with Mars and the other planets of this solar system, the equilibrium of the Sun will be disturbed and earthquakes will rock our planet. What super-mundane fate are we heading into, since our planet is so vulnerable, so dependent on the star of our system? And yet humans can only understand the immediate environment of their rapidly decaying world.

I experienced the thoughtless selfishness of humanity when we returned to Johannesburg, and we had to struggle alone and abandoned. Oh, how alone one can be in this crowded world when one suddenly realizes there is nobody—nobody in all the world—to turn to in one's hour of need. One is really alone, and the devastating realization explodes in the mind like a nightmare. Family, friends and strangers are all cast in one mold—indifferent, detached, unaware of one's struggle for existence in a hostile world.

The horror of struggling for David and myself in the noisy racket and smog of a hostile city proved too much for me, and I became ill. The cold hand of fear would grip my heart as I lay awake in the night and wondered what would become of us and where our next meal would come from. There was only enough money in the bank to pay the rent and keep a roof over our heads for another month, and I experienced what millions of others on this planet suffer in their struggle for existence in a cruel economic system. I maintained an outward calm, however, and David knew nothing of our close encounter with dire poverty. He was wonderful and kept my strength going through his care and consideration, despite being all day at school and up half the night with homework. He is indeed an advanced human being.

Knowing the meaning of starvation, one becomes aware of the dire sufferings of animals across this planet too. There are many beings without enough to eat while people eat their fill and gorge on the delights of food. What does one do when one has no money for sustenance in a world like this? What does one do when one has no home to shelter in and the people one knows and helped in the past pass by uncaring or unknowing? As long as they themselves are all right, they continue to step on others to gain their daily bread, denying the right of bread to others by their selfish, acquisitive habits, guarding their land and possessions like creatures of the lower planes.

Unable to turn to fellow humans in my hour of need, I turned to the universe instead. I knew the universe never takes one thing away unless something else is given.

The Major had called a few days previously. I had fainted at work in the airless bookshop, with a storm raging outside, and I had been worried about David's getting home from school. The Major sent me home in a taxi and told me not to go back to work. He brought us a large hamper of delicious food and a bottle of champagne. He must have been keeping a watch on me all the time, I thought. He must have known of our desperate plight as I struggled to work to keep a roof over our heads. But my strength was going. A hemorrhage set in, and he rushed me to the hospital where they tied me up with drips and injections in preparation for a major operation early the next morning. The Major stayed with me, never leaving my side until they wheeled me into the operating theater.

As death touched my heart again, I could clearly see into the time field of the future. I knew my reincarnation cycle on this planet was nearly at an end and my life would turn full cycle and take me back to Meton, where I could remain with Akon as I had in a previous life on Venus. The truth spread the warmth of its enfolding wings about me. No matter what happened on this planet, I would never be alone again. I belonged to Akon—I was born of his race. Death held no fear for me, but only a blessed release from the confines of Earth's time and the cycle of reincarnation here, where humankind is on a lower plane of existence.

There Is No Death, but Merely a Transition to Energy of the Life Field and Back to Matter Again in the Cycle of Life.

One evening, I opened my eyes to see the Major bending over the stark white hospital bed. His face was gentle and concerned, and his eyes were full of love as he looked into my eyes. I held out my hand and thanked him for all he had done. He clasped my hand in both his warm, firm hands.

"Go to sleep now," he said. "Don't worry any more. I'm going to look after you both from now on. Everything will be taken care of." And he bent over still more and kissed me.

David came to the other side of the bed and kissed me. His arm was in plaster, cradled in a sling.

"Oh," I sighed, then fainted again.

Then, as if from a great distance, I heard him say, "It's all right, Mom. Only a broken wrist when I fell over the hurdles at school. I'm staying with Peter and his family, and they are taking wonderful care of me."

The acute, burning pain of the hysterectomy incision brought me around again, and I saw the sister coming with a hypodermic syringe held high. She pulled down the bedclothes and jabbed me in the buttocks with the blunt needle, which hurt. With a sigh, I closed my eyes and floated away into the dreamless sleep of the drug she had given me.

"Was I dreaming, or did the Major and my son come here last evening?" I asked the sister next morning.

"Indeed they did, and what a charming, handsome gentleman the Major is." She sighed. "He left these beautiful red roses for you, and said he would be taking you home soon, where he will nurse you back to health again. In fact, here he is now. I will leave you alone together."

She arranged the roses in a vase beside the bed. Their fragrance filled the ward with hope again. Although it meant being netted completely into the military machine, at least I would be taken care of. I felt sure that Akon had seen to that. The sick politics of the world had disgusted me beyond measure and I wanted nothing more to do with them. Politics was being used by the barbarians of this world.

People of Earth will one day search within the skies of truth. They will find the distant shores of a glorious land, bathed by the seas of eternity and blessed by the glory of light from three stars. There, the great white seabirds circle ever higher in the dark sapphire blue of the sky, ever upward until they appear as mere specks in the far reach of the day. The music of the spheres vibrates through the air in harmony with the birds' flight as their vast white wings stretch out to gain even greater height over the dark blue seas. Up, up into the ice blue of the higher sky, where the directional pull is found, the white seabirds move with the tides of music to other isles set in the deep sapphire seas.

The dancing rhythm of all life is attuned to the song of the universe. The eternal dance of the micro-atoms streams out from stars, and life is generated on myriad Earths within a galaxy where the limitless tracts beyond are kept within bounds by the minimum temperature of the trackless void.

The spark of life within a planet is the residue of a star. All planets are cooled-down stars in their everlasting process of evolution from mass to density. The volcanic breath within them forms the light of the atmosphere, which creates life through its interaction with radiation from the stars. This radiation collides with the molecules of planetary atmospheres to create the immortal light of electricity, and the animated particles wriggle and writhe throughout the radiant atmosphere, each with its own bright electric charge.

The divine essence of life continues always. The soul awakens to knowledge in the higher spheres where the soul or life field is attracted to a planet evolved in a similar magnetic field and where one can be born again into matter or denser vibrations from the energy of death. It is merely a transition, a metamorphosis in all living things. There is no death, but merely a transition to energy of the life field and back to matter again in the cycle of life.

A planet's firmament holds humankind within the bond of life, and the glory of the universe is humanity's heritage. Humankind will soar into the splendor of star-filled space as the stars shed their radiance to help us find this glorious road to the stars. Humanity will come out of this world, will come out of the shadows of strife and will move with the winds of space to other planets in the light of the universe, where no minor discord can darken the glory of light.

We can create harmony throughout the fathomless depths of interstellar space where our minds can reach out to contact other minds in telepathic communication. The spatial void acts as a transmitter when one tunes in on the same wavelength. Wisdom and love combine with immortality within this universal unity to produce a highly evolved human being who is a part of eternity, existing within that divine spark of intelligence that pervades the entire universe, that harmonious and orderly rhythm called God.

I have known love in all its radiant splendor. My heart has awakened to its glow, forever nourished by the golden waves of light, so that I might reach out and encompass others to give them strength, courage and incentive to live on in a world fast becoming more and more dangerous to exist in.

As hydrogen clouds spin and condense into stars and planets, dust clouds are pushed out from the nucleus of our Milky Way galaxy. They form the vast spiral storm in the silky darkness of outer space. They reflect the rose red of divine light in the creation of stars and planets to harbor life within its shell of speeding light, where we all have our being—all made out of stardust.

Flowers for the author in Weisbaden.

THE ALPHA AND OMEGA OF ALL THINGS

I t is more than twenty-one years since Akon landed on the top of Flying Saucer Hill in his beautiful spaceship of light. Our son, Ayling, is now nineteen years old in Earth time. And yet they have come back. They have not forgotten me. I have lived on borrowed time for twenty years in order to complete this book and bring the knowledge of our environment in the universe to the people of this planet. We live in a vast and awesome universe, but its magnificence can be understood, loved and tamed by harmony. We can think and pick up clues to work out our destiny in this solar system as an energy crisis looms ever closer. Humans of Earth deplete the fossil fuels that have served them so faithfully. Earth has been giving of its bounty through the pastures of time—nature provides, but humankind continues to divide.

The truth in all its simplicity will be found in the pages of this book. These truths have always been. They are universal, and if humankind can learn to abide by them, perhaps this book can set the example. There is always a reason and an answer to all things in the universe. If only people would think, we could find its bounty.

I have found its bounty in all its glorious and magnificent providence. It is simple and free, an intelligent energy that can be manipulated and controlled, loved and trusted. That bounty is light, the electromagnetic wavelength of our galaxy. It has given harmony to the most beloved places, such as the farm, Whyteleafe, at Rosetta, where Flying Saucer Hill rears up like a guardian mountain with the dip in the top, where my late sister and her wonderful husband lived for so many years, and where Akon first found me waiting for him on the mountaintop.

Whyteleafe is now owned and cared for, and made more beautiful than ever, by a lovely family of very old friends, related to me through marriage. They have taken over the farms, improved the entire country-side and made a great success out of their project by constructing a series of lakes down the great valley and planting pine trees over the hillsides.

What happiness it was to know that Akon had come back, even for so short a time! How the places he touched all changed for the better! The heights of Cathkin are now part of a beautiful reserve, protected by the government, where only authorized persons are allowed to pass through the security gates. Further away, Flying Saucer Hill has been left untouched by the destructive hand of humankind, protected and cared for by good, civilized people. Where my cottage had been in Parktown, a beautiful park now spreads its joy for the people of Johannesburg.

Good comes out of all things when the contacts are right and the people are in harmony. The steep, southern slopes of Flying Saucer Hill tumble into the blue waters of the lake where the wild geese and the ducks skim over the tranquil surface to land and nest in the reeds and willows bordering the far distances of shoreline. I was invited back there, to the rolling hills of my childhood days, and we all celebrated with a delicious luncheon and Rhine wines. I was taken up the slopes of Flying Saucer Hill in a Land Rover, as I could not walk up it anymore because of my heart condition. My hosts were all so wonderful and made me feel that I had really come home again.

Akon's spaceship hovered over the mountaintop and the excitement was electric. My hosts telephoned other people in the area to tell them to look for the spaceship and watch for it before the mist came down over the hills. I heard the Zulu call out, their voices echoing in the hills, "God has come." The Land Rover was fitted with a two-way radio, so the message went out.

I saw Akon again as he came to my side by means of a light ray projected in a three-dimensional image of simple patterns of electronic charges. He was a projection, but I saw him as if in real life—the illusion of his human presence was perfect but for the sensations of touch and smell. By means of this laser light, Akon was able to project three-dimensional images of himself and Ayling to speak to me and reassure me of his constant love and thoughts. The proximity of the tube of light in which they were standing felt like the electric mirage had when I had approached its curtain in the mothership, and a prickling sensation rippled through my body.

"Oh," I said to them, "can't I come too, even in the laser light, rather than stay here?"

"Not at present," Akon said gently. "But within the next five years of Earth time, my beloved."

Ayling blew me a kiss with his hand. He was as tall and agile as his father and his face was breathtakingly handsome, with an unusual and fascinating beauty. Straight golden hair hung to his shoulders and his golden eyes looked into mine with deep love. But the whole image faded away, and there was nothing left. Heartbroken, I turned away. No wonder my heart is now so sorely affected. For the second time, I allowed emotion to take its toll. The first time was many years ago, when my friend Neslie comforted me. She has remained my dearest friend ever since.

This was a lesson for me to learn—to understand that change and the process of creation go on forever, and that one must move with the constant change and evolution of the universe. Nothing is ever static. Nothing remains the same. In this way, by realizing that, one moves in harmony and becomes ageless by accepting the inevitable destiny of all things in a changing universe.

Akon keeps a constant watch and surveillance on our Sun and our solar system. It is not static and finished—it is still being formed, still evolving. A second star will one day light up our solar system. The black and orange atmospheric bands of Jupiter's disk cover a warming furnace in which thermonuclear reactions have already started. Thus Jupiter radiates life-giving light to its family of small planets, while a vast vortex storm, the beginnings of sunspots or star material triggered off by magnetism, forms the vast red spot that astronomers have pondered for centuries.

Humankind now must learn to adapt to a higher vibratory rate as our atmosphere changes within the forming binary system. Cosmic rays will intensify with the radiation from two stars affecting Earth's climate in dramatic and awesome ways. The outer aspiring stars—Saturn, Uranus and Neptune—continue to evolve and generate life-giving light to their families of surrounding planets, satellites and debris. They will form still more solar systems as they mature and light up into stars, and as life is generated within by everlasting change. All planets are cooled-down stars. Moons, asteroids, comets and other rocky fragments are merely the debris of stars—pieces of star failure.

All things have a reason for being—even black holes, which have bugged scientists for years. These are pockets of minimum temperature within the galaxy where light cannot penetrate vortex residues that are highly dangerous and can suck any substance or energy into their whirl-pool gravitation. Spaceships avoid them because the unified field propulsion systems would be nullified by such an encounter. Therefore, spaceships move around the equatorial perimeter of such anomalies within the electromagnetic plasma of the galaxy.

THE UNIVERSE OF LIGHT NEVER TAKES ONE THING AWAY UNLESS SOMETHING ELSE IS GIVEN.

I have experienced the effects of a higher vibratory rate from the light of three stars. I know what it will mean to life within the Sun's system as the entire collection of stars, planets, moons, asteroids and debris moves into the higher octaves of existence, toward its destiny within the Milky Way galaxy. Humans of this system have always thought of their existence as the alpha and omega of all things. Their consciousness is barely able to absorb the simplicity of their environment. Mathematical monstrosities are not necessary to explain it all, but their complicated science develops still more into a monster of mathematics and machines.

The knowledge of the universe has always existed. Even the Greeks knew of the unified field within the electromagnetic wavelength of light, which comprises all of creation. They brought it into their alphabet. Alpha, beta, gamma, delta—a harmonic sound to interact with the four forces of light, the rhythm resonating within our brains. This will give us the alpha rhythm of achievement where equanimity maintains a part of everyday life so long as no conflict is involved.

Universal harmonics is the mathematics used by Akon's civilization. He speaks of harmonic maths, an harmonic affinity with all substance, a resonance tuned to matter itself expressed in terms of light. A simple equation gives us the answer to the unified field propulsion systems for interstellar spaceships. A unified field equation of seven-figure harmonics is the key to space travel.

This simple equation is clear in my mind. The harmonic of antigravity through the harmonic of light being doubled, alters the geometric of time, and our awareness of reality in the physical sense will shift from one spatial point to another. This is based on space-time geometries within the unified field that permeates all of existence.

Of all the many thousands of Earth's scientists, only Einstein could find the simplicity of the universe in his harmonic equation, $E = mc^2$. He achieved this by maintaining a fairly continuous alpha rhythm, keeping his brain in patterns of relaxed attention. Look what came out of it, though—the atomic bomb, the destruction of material substance and its conversion into pure energy.

Akon, as a great physicist, can reverse the process. Physical substance in any desired shape is produced from pure energy, hence the atomic structure of the interstellar spaceships of light, which are completely smooth and all in one piece. The composition of the material of the spaceship conducts energy to generate the unified field propulsion systems. As a natural celestial object, it achieves a shift in space and time in the frequency of light, which is so very different to the nuts-and-bolts flying saucers constructed by people of Earth, which are purely atmospheric craft and propelled by jets.

Akon's spaceship resonates at harmonics tuned to light between the two cycles of matter and antimatter manifesting in alternate pulses. Therefore, it moves instantaneously through the double cycle within the electromagnetic wavelength of the universe. It uses the fabric of space itself, altering the space-time geometric matrix. The spaceship acts as a protection for the people within it as it changes position through the unified field. We are all creatures of light, composed of micro-atoms, the ultimate particle. We are built up from a combination of wavelengths of the creative force, which we call light—or God.

The universe of light never takes one thing away, but something else is given. My grandson Astley, my daughter's child, is now four years old. He is another golden boy, whose blue-gray eyes already have the look of distance, the look of intelligent wisdom that sees beyond the limited horizons of earthbound people. Other star children have been born to friends who named them Akon or Pleia, immortalizing my beloved and my dear friends from outer space.

And what about the planet Earth? Can its teeming billions survive in such a small and vulnerable world? Can their mass leveling and conformity produce leaders to solve the many problems they will face within the next five years, so that they might survive their time and live into ours and join our community of galactic civilizations? The nucleus of our galaxy emits a stream of energy—the light we are all made out of. The release of micro-atoms of light from oxygen is the source of all life, and micro-atoms in greater unities are equal to atoms. All of creation is light . . .

With love,

Elizabeth Klarer.

CRITIQUE: A CHRISTIAN'S PERSPECTIVE

A s the author's son and as a Christian, I have discerned a need to briefly communicate some of my personal views and thoughts in the hope that these will help those readers seeking truth to gain a perspective on the choice between Christianity and aspects of the philosophy in this book, which I believe to be essentially New Age (references to reincarnation, telepathy, harmony or wholeness with the universe, tuning in with the infinite, the interstellar human family, the definition of God and so on). Many people pose the question "Is there life after death?" and are seeking answers about life's purpose—both of these quests are answered by scripture. There are major differences between New Age philosophy and Christianity, but these I will not try to cover here, as they are too complex to address briefly.

Although my mother's writings come across as New Age, there are a number of Biblical parallels that can be identified. For instance:

- Near the end of chapter 3 she states, "One cannot expect everything to be handed over on a plate if one has not the requisites for knowledge, understanding, harmony, love and discipline—without fear." Christian teaching is that we must also grow in this way, but by God's grace, with faith as the key.
- The book is about love, which is also a major theme of the New Testament.
- In chapter 4 there is reference to a divine energy (God, by definition) creating life, and also a statement that we are all evolved from stardust. This compares favorably to Genesis chapters 1 and 2. Also in chapter 4 she writes:

"The level of civilization of races and peoples can only be measured by their degree of compassion," which is another important Biblical theme.

- Her warnings on the environment in chapter 7—"through stupidity and ignorance, humans are destroying their natural environment," for example—are reinforced by the responsibility placed on us by God to look after the Earth (Genesis 1: 26–28). To quote the *Believer's Bible Commentary* by William MacDonald: "God gave man a mandate to subdue creation and have dominion over it—to use it but not to abuse it. The modern crises in the earth's environment are due to man's greed, selfishness and carelessness." My mother also refers to there being thirty years left for the survival of Earth. She would have written this circa 1977 or before—a prediction not yet fulfilled, but seemingly well on the way.
- The statement in chapter 5, "For only the pure in heart shall see the universe," could be an allusion to "Blessed are the pure in heart, for they shall see God" (Matthew 5:8).
- In *Beyond the Light Barrier*, God is defined in a number of ways, notably: "where all men experience a state of union with the universe, or to them, God," "the great intelligence of the universe," "the eternal presence within that divine spark of intelligence that pervades the entire universe," "that harmonious and orderly rhythm called God" and "the creative force, which we call light." Scripture tells us that the Holy Spirit (God) is separate to and over and above His creation. He is infinite, personal and loving, but just and holy.

In the introduction, my mother says, "This book is about time." I think it is more about love. As she states in chapter 4, "Love is a force, a being who needs understanding, for love is the electric force of life. Love is the flame of eternal beauty." She also writes, "To love all things is to enfold oneself within the magnetic field of positive existence, to commune and become one with nature and live in harmony with the universe." This book is a story of love, and a warning to humankind. It is a plea for change in negative thinking and attitudes, away from selfishness and self-desire, immorality, violence, environmental destruction and war.

Unfortunately, materialism, corruption, crime and immorality are rampant in this world. I can only agree with my mother when she writes critically in chapter 5, "A different kind of people must evolve on Earth. A new species of human must appear: people of understanding, love and tolerance, who are set on life rather than violence and death, who will become the children of their God, the children of the universe in harmony with all nature." Although she refers to "their God," she admits that to become children of God is the way to spiritual salvation. Interestingly, a few weeks before my mother passed on in 1994, she ostensibly accepted Jesus Christ as her savior, after I presented the Gospel to her.

There is no reference to Christ as a way of spiritual survival. Rather the question is asked at the end of chapter 4, "Is it not possible even now to show people of Earth the way to spiritual and scientific survival?" The reference to "their God" infers a clash with scripture, which motivates a single true living God and creator of the universe.

She refers to the seeking of help for men of Earth—perhaps salvation from an advanced people from beyond our skies. However, this salvation is right here on Earth for each and every one of us through the Holy Spirit—the creator Himself and His incarnation. Some people I have spoken to get a feeling of hope from her story of other alien races out there who will come to our aid, but this hope (I believe) is misplaced and must be put fair and square in the creator of the universe Himself.

I have no conclusive proof as to the truth of her story but continue to keep an open mind, although as a Christian there are conflicts for me. I saw UFOs in my teens, and so I know they exist. I had many years of involvement with my mother's UFO interest, attending meetings, lectures, and sky watches, before I turned to God and Christianity. However, for me the credibility of the story is adversely influenced by a few inaccuracies, a major one being my own involvement (I must have been about ten years old) in the chapter 5 event dealing with a horse ride near Cathkin in the Drakensberg. This involved a landing of the spaceship across the path and a meeting with Akon. Other than the horse ride, I can recall none of this. Another instance is in her epilogue, when Akon apparently promises to return for her in five years—but this promise is seemingly unfulfilled, as the year of this writing would have been circa 1977 (she refers to Astley as being four years old, and he was born 1973) and she was still very much around from 1982 on. No matter the credibility of the alien interaction, to my mind the book's philosophy of love, compassion and caring for our environment (the issue of global warming looms) is paramount. It may well have been a major objective and ideal of hers to present her philosophy, via this story, to a struggling humanity (and she mentions this in chapter 6).

She also states her objective of bringing the truth of the universe to Earth people. The light of the universe (God) stepped down into darkness (via Jesus Christ) to bring understanding to all those who would receive it. It has become clear to me that if man had followed God's word (the Bible), the world would not be in the predicament it's in now: wars, poverty, pollution, disease, global warming. Do we need an alien race (if indeed it exists) to show us the way, when we already have it through God's word and His son (incarnation in the flesh)? Contrary to New Age belief, fear of the Lord is the deeply sane recognition that we are not God and cannot be God.

My mother was a wonderful person who lived out her life as a gentle, caring and loving human being. Often I wish she was here today so that I could ask her so many of the questions I did not think to ask when she was still alive. I hope that the reader has benefited in some way from this epilogue, bearing in mind that the truth that will save mankind has already been presented to Earth people through the ancient scriptures.

David J. Klarer
Pinetown, South Africa
May 2007

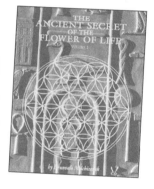
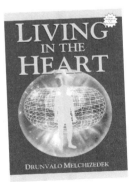

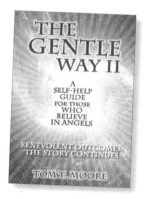

☥ Light Technology PUBLISHING *Presents*

The Ultimate UFO series
THROUGH ROBERT SHAPIRO

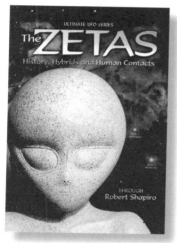

$24.95 • Softcover • 480 PP.
ISBN 978-1-891824-36-4

THE ZETAS
History, Hybrids, and Human Contacts

The beings on Zeta Reticuli are the future selves — granted, several million years in the future — of the beings on Earth right now. On the soul line, this has to do with your evolution to become more, to be more established benevolently on a creative level. By the time your souls become those Zeta Reticulian beings several million years in the future, you will be able to interact with all life in the most benevolent way while being strongly intellectual and scientific.

In this way, your science will have a complete balance with heart and soul. This is one of the greatest aspects of significance between you and the Zeta Reticulian beings as of this time. So to them, you are their past lives — that's why they're so fascinated with you — but for you, when you interact with these beings, you are truly meeting, in many senses, your future.

— Zoosh

ANDROMEDA

The Andromedans tell what really happened on their journeys and on Earth. They clear up questions one might have after reading *UFO Contact from Andromeda: Extraterrestrial Prophecy* — the inspiring text of which follows the channeling in this book. In addition, they supply a lively account of their lives on their home planet in the Andromedan constellation of our galaxy.

Crew members of the ship who speak include
- Leia, the beautiful cultural specialist and social diplomat
- Cheswa, the cultural liaison
- G-dansa, Leia's daughter
- Duszan, the Junior Scientist
- Onzo, the Senior Scientist and Crew Leader, the youngest (yet genetically modified to be the most brilliant) of the crew
- Playmate, a two-foot-tall, roly-poly Andromedan who teaches communion of heart and mind

$16.95 • Softcover • 464 PP.
ISBN 978-1-891824-35-7

THROUGH ROBERT SHAPIRO

The EXPLORER RACE and ISIS

Explorer Race Book 8

This book addresses the Creator in all of you and speaks directly to stimulate the benevolence of that energy you are all built on. Creator School is the place where the energy that precedes creators comes from so that creators can create their ability, their energy, and their capacity to manifest. It is my intention to speak not only about the seen and the unseen but also, from time to time, about the unimagined.

— Isis

This amazing book includes priestess training, shamanic training, Isis adventures with Explorer Race beings — before Earth and on Earth — and an incredibly expanded explanation of the dynamics of the Explorer Race. Isis is the prototypal loving, nurturing, guiding feminine being, the focus of feminine energy. She has the ability to expand limited thinking without making people with limited beliefs feel uncomfortable.

She is a fantastic storyteller, and all her stories are teaching stories. If you care about who you are, why you are here, where you are going, and what life is all about — pick up this book. You won't lay it down until you are through, and then you will want more.

THE **EXPLORER RACE** AND

ISIS

THROUGH
ROBERT SHAPIRO

$14.95 • Softcover • 352 PP.
978-1-891824-11-1

Chapters Include

- Isis and Your Creator
- The Biography of Isis
- The Planetary Influence of Isis
- The Adventurer
- Soul Colors and Shapes
- Creation Mechanics
- The Insect Form and Fairies
- Orion's Transition and Its Application to Earth
- The Veil and the Blue Portal
- The Goddess and the Natural Feminine
- Self-Violence and Self-Love
- The Concept of Mutual Benefit

THROUGH ROBERT SHAPIRO

The EXPLORER RACE and JESUS

Explorer Race Book 9

In this book, I will make an effort to speak of who I really am, where I'm from, what I'm doing now, why I went to Earth, what I hoped to accomplish, what I did accomplish, and perhaps other things. I want to try to explain why things happened, why people did "this" or "that" during my lifetime. I will try to fill in details.

— Jesus

THE EXPLORER RACE AND

JESUS

through ROBERT SHAPIRO

$16.95 • Softcover • 352 PP.
978-1-891824-14-2

The immortal personality who lived the life we know as Jesus, along with his students and friends, describes with clarity and love his life and teaching on Earth 2,000 years ago.

These beings lovingly offer their experiences of the events that happened then and of Jesus's time-traveling adventures, especially to other planets and to the nineteenth and twentieth centuries, which he called the time of the machines — the time of troubles.

It is so heartwarming and interesting that you won't want to put it down.

Chapters Include
- Jesus's Home World, Their Love Creations, and the Four Who Visited Earth
- The "Facts" of Jesus's Life Here, His Future Return
- The Teachings and Travels
- A Student's Time with Jesus and His Tales of Jesus's Time Travels
- The Shamanic Use of the Senses
- Many Journeys, Many Disguises
- The Child Student Who Became a Traveling Singer-Healer
- Learning to Invite Matter to Transform Itself

☥ *Light Technology* PUBLISHING *Presents*

TO ORDER PRINT BOOKS
Visit LightTechnology.com, Call 928-526-1345 or 1-800-450-0985,
or Check Amazon.com or Your Favorite Bookstore

THROUGH ROBERT SHAPIRO

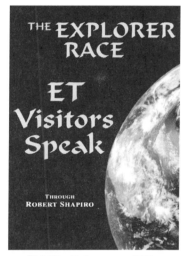

$14.95 • Softcover • 352 PP.
978-1-891824-28-9

ET Visitors Speak, Volume 1
Explorer Race Book 11

Even as you search the sky for extraterrestrials and their spaceships, ETs are here on planet Earth. They are stranded, visiting, exploring, studying culture, healing Earth of trauma (brought on by irresponsible activities such as mining), or researching the history of Christianity over the past 2,000 years.

Some are in human guise. Some are in spirit form. Some look like what we call animals, as they come from the species' home planet and interact with their fellow beings that we have labeled cats or cows or elephants. Some are brilliant cosmic mathematicians with a wonderful sense of humor and presently living here as penguins. Some are fledgling diplomats training for future postings on Earth when we have ET embassies here.

In this book, these fascinating beings share their thoughts, origins, and purposes for being here.

ET Visitors Speak, Volume 2
Explorer Race Book 15

For those of you who've always wanted to meet somebody completely different, here's your opportunity. This book contains the continuing adventures of visitors to planet Earth. In a strange sense, you might include yourself as one of them, as the human race does not really claim the title of full-time and permanent Earth citizens.

When you read this book, think about it as if you were visiting another planet. What would you say in reaction to the local population about their habits and so on? Put yourself in the picture so that this isn't just a meaningless travel log from various beings you don't know and may never meet.

Make it personal this time because the time is coming when you might just be one of those extraterrestrials on another planet. So you might as well practice now and get your lines down right.

$19.95 • Softcover • 512 PP.
978-1-891824-78-4

THROUGH ROBERT SHAPIRO

ETs on Earth, Volume 1 • Explorer Race Book 18

In the beginning of the Explorer Race adventure — that means you, all humans on Earth way back — ETs on Earth were a normal thing. In fact, you were ETs who came from many different planets those thousands of years ago, and you felt that Earth was a wonderful place where you could thrive.

I want you to keep that in mind when you read about these ETs who happen to be still visiting Earth. In this book, if you can keep that in mind, it will not be too surprising or shocking. In fact, most of you will be ETs again in another life, and your youngsters just might be ETs from Earth visiting other planets in the future.

This should be a fun read and a gentle reminder that ETs are just friends from some place — you might say from another neighborhood.

— Zoosh

$16.95 • Softcover • 352 PP.
978-1-891824-91-3

ETs on Earth, Volume 2 • Explorer Race Book 21

You've noticed lately — haven't you? — that for the past few years, UFOs and phenomena in the skies are all over the place. Well, hold on to your hats! You can be pretty sure this is only going to increase in its frequency in the skies. In this book, you'll be able to read a little bit about who the beings in the UFOs are, where they're from, why they're here, and so on.

In the future, it won't just be airplane pilots reporting on these things. You'll be talking about it among yourselves because regular folks just like you will be seeing these ships. This time, don't keep it quiet. Talk about it with your neighbors or your friends online. It gives other people permission to believe what they saw. People have been taught, you know, not to believe what they see. So you can believe it.

— Zoosh

$16.95 • Softcover • 416 PP.
978-1-62233-003-4

ETs on Earth, Volume 3 • Explorer Race Book 22

Many of you are ready to welcome ETs — if not in your personal lives, at least to interact with government bodies in large groups. Some of you are prepared to shake hands. Even a few want hugs. But it may not be that personal.

There are circumstances coming up now in your evolution toward your natural selves that make it almost imperative to have contact of a benevolent nature between Earth people and extraterrestrials. For now, many ETs are shy about coming here. They will, at some risk, show you images of themselves (in the skies, you will see them defined by clouds), or you will see something that reminds you of spaceships.

As your cousins, which is the way they see themselves (the ones you are most likely to meet), ETs recognize that you are a version of their extended family. You will find many reminders of who you might have been or who you might be in other lives or who your extended family is now.

$16.95 • Softcover • 352 PP.
978-1-62233-044-7

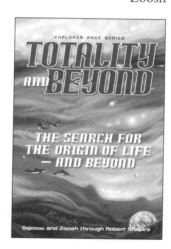

THROUGH ROBERT SHAPIRO

STEPS ON THE PATH OF
transformation
Volume I

Explorer Race Book 23

STEPS ON THE PATH OF
transformation
Volume I
channeled through Robert Shapiro

$19.95 • Softcover • 320 PP.
978-1-62233-045-4

As you read this material, this is what to keep in mind: Your path might be completely different from what this book attempts to show you. So when you read this material, don't think, "I can't possibly do that." Rather, think about what is familiar to you.

You will experience times when you have read a page or two and something feels as if it resonates within you. It might not be a sequence of words that you find in a paragraph. It could be words that came together from different paragraphs, creating in you a sense of familiarity. This tells you that these books are not just about thoughts or ideas. The books are about transformation.

Even if you have difficulty reading the books in the language they are in, go through them and put your hands on some of the pages, or touch the pages to your arms or other parts of your body to see whether the books — with all the words, letters, symbols, and numbers — can in some way trigger a dream, a vision, or a moment of inspiration in you that helps to bring about a better life for you and those around you.

Good luck, and good life in this pursuit.
— Isis

Chapters Include

- You Traverse to Your Home Planet in Deep Sleep

- Allowing Perception without Judgment Moves You to 3.56

- Old Ways of Life Fall Away, and Eden Is Ahead

- Shift Your Energy Production

- Adapt Now to Survive

- You Are Losing the Mask You Created to Survive

- You Are Being Activated from Inside to Become Your Spirit Self in Your Day-to-Day Life

THROUGH ROBERT SHAPIRO

ETS FROM UFO CASEBOOK'S BEST PICTURES SPEAK

Explorer Race Book 25

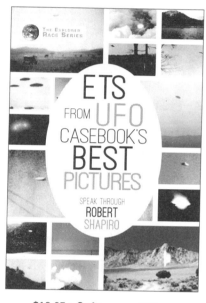

$16.95 • Softcover • 320 PP.
978-1-62233-058-4

This book is for those who are interested in things that are new, different, exciting, or mysterious. Perhaps you will discover your likes and dislikes are not only associated with Earth and your personality, family, and friends. Some of it might actually be associated with your extraterrestrial roots!

All of you on Earth, all you human beings, have extraterrestrial roots. If you trace the Earth-human DNA back far enough, it goes to other planets. The reason you're not aware of this or able to prove it scientifically in published papers is that what little is known about this on your planet is largely kept secret.

As you read these pages, you will discover that your brothers, sisters, cousins, aunties, uncles, friends, and relations are not only on Earth. They are on other planets too.

— Zoosh

Chapters Include
- The Mirror Universe
- Pay Kindness Forward
- Earth Humans Will Return to Their Natural State
- All Life on Earth Is Transforming to Benevolence
- Opening the Heart Includes Opening Perception
- You Are Made Up of Where You Are
- Women Balance the Passage of Discomfort
- Home Is Wherever Light and Love Exist

‍Light Technology PUBLISHING Presents

TO ORDER PRINT BOOKS
Visit LightTechnology.com, Call 928-526-1345 or 1-800-450-0985,
or Check Amazon.com or Your Favorite Bookstore

SHAMANIC SECRETS SERIES
THROUGH ROBERT SHAPIRO

Shamanic Secrets: Lost Wisdom Regained

Due to wars, natural disasters, a shaman not being able to train a successor, and many other reasons, Isis (through Robert) says that 95 percent of the accumulated shamanic wisdom has been lost. Now it is important to regain this wisdom as young people who are able to learn and use these processes are being born now.

Beings who lived as shamans and healers on Earth at various times now speak through Robert Shapiro and bring these lost teachings and techniques to a humanity waking up and discovering it has the talents and abilities to use this wisdom for the benefit of all.

$16.95 • Softcover • 352 PP. • ISBN 978-1-62233-049-2

Shamanic Secrets for Material Mastery

Explore the heart and soul connection between humans and Mother Earth. Through that intimacy, miracles of healing and expanded awareness can flourish.
$19.95 • Softcover • 528 PP.
978-1-891824-12-8

Shamanic Secrets for Physical Mastery

The purpose of this book is to explain the sacred nature of the physical body and some of the magnificent gifts it offers.
$25.00 • Softcover • 608 PP.
978-1-891824-29-6

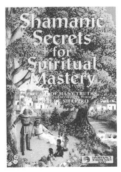

Shamanic Secrets for Spiritual Mastery

Spiritual mastery is the underpinnings of multiple ways of being, understanding, appreciating, and interacting in harmony with your world.
$29.95 • Softcover • 768 PP.
978-1-891824-58-6

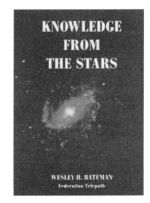

𝔏ight Technology PUBLISHING Presents

BOOKS THROUGH TINA LOUISE SPALDING

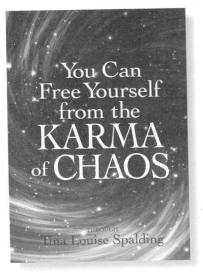

You Can Free Yourself from the Karma of Chaos

We have come here as a group to help you because it is a pivotal time in your planet's evolution. You are seeing monumental changes in your society now. To achieve the shifts that these transfigurations will bring about, you must understand your minds, histories, and human nature as you experience it on the ground, in your hearts, and in your consciousnesses.

Your baggage, judgments, and fears must be released for you to enter this new world, this new time on your planet, with clear and uncontaminated minds. It is our purpose to bring you through this journey so that you will understand, forgive, and walk unencumbered into your new future.

— Ananda

$16.95 • Softcover • 224 pp. • 978-1-62233-057-7

   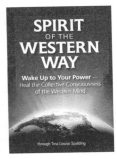

Jesus: My Autobiography
$16.95 • Softcover • 304 pp.
978-1-62233-030-0

Love and a Map to the Unaltered Soul
$16.95 • Softcover • 240 pp.
ISBN 978-1-62233-047-8

Making Love to God: The Path to Divine Sex
$19.95 • Softcover • 416 pp.
978-1-62233-009-6

Great Minds Speak to You
$19.95 • Softcover • 192 pp.
Includes CD
978-1-62233-010-2

Spirit of the Western Way: Wake Up to Your Power — Heal the Collective Consciousness of the Western Mind
$16.95 • Softcover • 176 pp.
978-1-62233-051-5

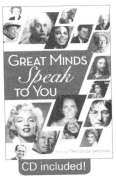